PROPRIOCEPTIVE CONTROL OF HUMAN MOVEMENT

THE HUMAN MOVEMENT SERIES
General Editor: H.T.A. Whiting

Human Movement - a field of study

Edited by: J.D. BROOKE and H.T.A. WHITING

Readings in Sports Physchology.

Edited by: H.T.A. WHITING

Readings in the Aesthetics of Sport.

Edited by: H.T.A. WHITING

Personality and Performance in Physical Education and Sport.

By: H.T.A. WHITING, K. HARDMAN, L.B. HENDRY and MARILYN G. JONES

Concepts in Modern Educational Dance.

By: H.B. REDFERN

Techniques for the Analysis of Human Movement.

By: O.W. GRIEVE, Doris MILLER, D. MITCHELSON, T. PAUL and A. J. SMITH

Themes for Educational Gymnastics.

By: JEAN WILLIAMS

Expression in Movement and the Arts.

By: DAVID BEST

PROPRIOCEPTIVE CONTROL OF HUMAN MOVEMENT

by

JOHN DICKINSON, Ph.D.,
Psychology Department,
St. Francis Xavier University.

LEPUS BOOKS

London 1974

The Author

John Dickinson is an Associate Professor in the Psychology Department, St. Francis Xavier University, Antigonish, Nova Scotia, Canada. He graduated from Birmingham University with an Honours B.A. in Combined Subjects. After training as a teacher at Birmingham University, he went on to study for a Ph.D. in Psychology at Nottingham University. Dr. Dickinson was a teaching fellow at Loughborough College of Education between 1968 and 1970 when he moved to his present position.

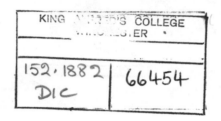
Standard Book Number 86019 002 1

Computer Typesetting by Print Origination,
Bootle, Merseyside, L20 6NS
Printed by Unwin Bros., Woking, Surrey
Bound by T. & A. Constable Ltd., Edinburgh.

To Miss B.N. Knapp, and the late Dr. J.A. Leonard.

CONTENTS

ACKNOWLEDGEMENTS

The author is indebted to the following publishers and authors who have given permission for material to be used in this book.

Fig. 1. is reproduced by permission of The Company of Biologists Limited, Department of Zoology, Downing Street, Cambridge, England.

Fig. 2. is reproduced by permission of S. Karger AG Basel.

Fig. 3. is reproduced by permission of John Wiley and Sons Limited.

Fig. 4. is reproduced by kind permission of Cambridge University Press.

Fig. 5. is reproduced by permission of the editors of the Proceedings of the National Academy of Science.

Fig. 7. is reproduced by permission of Prentice-Hall Inc.

Fig. 8. is reproduced by permission of Charles C. Thomas, Publisher.

Figs. 11, 20 and 21, are reproduced by permission of the Managing Editor of the Journal of Motor Behavior.

Fig. 12. is reproduced by permission of W. H. Freeman and Company for Scientific American, Inc.

Fig. 13. is reproduced by permission of the American Psychological Association and Dr. E. A. Fleishman.

Figs. 14 and 15, are reproduced by permission of the American Psychological Association and Dr. E. A. Fleishman.

Fig. 16 is reproduced by permission of the Editor, British Journal of Psychology.

Fig. 17. is reproduced by permission of the American Psychological Association and Dr. J. A. Adams.

Figs. 18 and 19, are reproduced by permission of the American Psychological Association and Dr. M. I. Posner.

Fig. 22. is reprinted with permission from Pergamon Press Ltd. and Dr. D. H. Holding.

Fig. 23. is reprinted with permission from the Editors, Ergonomics, Taylor and Francis, Ltd.

Plates 1 and 2, are reproduced by courtesy of Lafayette Instrument Company.

ACKNOWLEDGEMENTS

PREFACE

Over a number of years evidence has been accumulating concerning the way in which human movements are learned and performed. One part of this evidence is concerned with the feedback from proprioceptors which accompany movement and the way in which this information is relevant to the control of activity. Research has proceeded along several different fronts. Some investigators have been concerned with learning, others with performance, some with pure physiological aspects and others with perception. This book is an attempt to bring a proportion of this evidence together in a single source. It is hoped that anyone involved in these inter-related aspects of human movement will find at least some sections of interest to them. It would be nice to claim that the book also integrates information from contributing disciplines. To some extent this has been an objective, but integration of information requires some homogeneity of empirical technique and data. Attempts at providing a single viewpoint from which studies concerning proprioception may be considered necessarily require either ignoring much relevant and important information or making illegitimate comparisons between studies which have different basic assumptions. The strategy within the book has been to present information in the context of the viewpoint of the discipline from which it derived. With this in mind, comparisons have been made where it has been considered legitimate. Readers may find additional similarities, contradictions and inferences in considering the evidence from different disciplines.

The book is intended for those who have at least some basic knowledge of human anatomy and physiology as well as an acquaintance with the scientific method of experimenting with human subjects. Advanced undergraduates in those disciplines concerned with human movement should not find the material too complex.

A recurring difficulty in the preparation of the book has been making decisions concerning the amount of background detail to provide for specific study areas. Compromises have been necessary in maintaining a balance between the background and the evidence related specifically to proprioception. It is hoped that the background material is sufficient for reasonable evaluations of the evidence to be made and yet not so disproportionately detailed that the theme of the work is lost. The reader who is more familiar with the material may find it preferable to skip these background sections whereas those less familiar may wish to pursue some of the references to alternative sources. The background material is stated only once and reference is made to this in future consideration. It is perfectly possible that alternative arrangements of the material would be acceptable.

I am extremely conscious at the time of writing, of the high rate of publication of relevant studies. Many important contributions to this field have been made in the two years since the idea for this book was conceived. Where speculation has been made in the absence of empirical fact, it is probable that solid evidence will be available soon. The large number of studies currently available has also meant that some selection of material has been necessary. The personal nature of the selection process means that some authors may feel that their work has been unjustifiably neglected. I should appreciate receiving criticisms and comments on the book, and apologize in advance for what is perhaps a reflection of my own biases and interests in the selection of material.

I am indebted to Drs G. Brooks, P. Henke, K. den Heyer, R. Johnson, E. Pencer and M. Schwartz for reading and criticizing sections of the manuscript, and to my wife for considerable assistance in its preparation. My thanks are due to St. Francis Xavier University who supported the writing of this book with a summer stipend and a University Council of Research grant. Acknowledgements are also made to authors and publishers who allowed material to be reprinted and of whom a detailed list is provided.

John Dickinson,
St. Francis Xavier University,
Antigonish, Nova Scotia,
Canada.
1973.

1

HISTORICAL REVIEW

Chapter

1 HISTORICAL REVIEW

Human movement is an eclectic area of study, drawing its content from several related disciplines. Psychology, physical education, physiology and ergonomics all contribute to knowledge of the ways in which people move and the factors controlling or involved in learning movement. Thus the study of any particular aspect of human movement must utilize all related disciplinary sources. Although interdisciplinary study is becoming common, it presents certain problems, not least of which is the question of terminology. The term proprioception is used frequently in each of the disciplines and yet it tends to be considered by each in the light of that discipline's own historical development and in the context of experiments typical of that field. Because of this, the study of proprioception has been relatively uncoordinated and a precise and universally acceptable definition is not currently available. To establish a basis for the discussion of proprioception, the development of interest in this area and the controversy concerning the definition of the term will be described.

Historical Review

Historical treatments of the growth and development of knowledge in the field of proprioception are uncommon and amongst general histories of psychology, only Boring's 'Sensation and Perception in the History of Psychology' (1942) gives more than cursory attention to this particular problem. The present review is largely based on Boring's work and is consequently somewhat limited in its contribution. Surprisingly it appears that there was more interest in the nineteenth century in detailing the history of proprioceptive study. Many of the papers on this topic presented detailed reviews, and as early as 1846 Sir William Hamilton produced an account of the history of 'the muscle sense'. Whilst it may be surprising that serious consideration has not been given to the topic, particularly since the vast majority of scientifically based research into the subject has occurred only in

3

the last one hundred and fifty years, it is even more intriguing that there should exist discrepancies among sources concerning its development.

There is little doubt, however, about the origin of the term. In his Silliman Lectures, later published as one of the most influential physiological texts of this century ('The Integrative Action of the Nervous System', 1906), Sherrington coined the terms proprioception, interoception and exteroception. This tripartite division of the body's receptor systems has been explained many times. In summary, the exteroceptors—the ears, nose, eyes, mouth and skin are designated as those receptors whose stimuli have their origins outside the body. The interoceptors, on the other hand, are those located in the visceral organs. The stimuli for these receptors are changes occuring in the deep field of the body. Finally, proprioception is considered to be the awareness of movement derived from muscular, tendonous, articular and vestibular receptors. Considerable research and speculation had preceded Sherrington, however, and the identification of those receptors which he classified as proprioceptors had occured some decades earlier.

Not surprisingly, initial interest in the 'muscle sense' came from philosophers rather than psychologists or physiologists. Boring (1942) related that the possibility of such a phenomenon was mentioned by Descartes. He suggested that distance perception was partially a result of the information derived from the muscles of visual control. A similar point of view was described by Berkely in the early eighteenth century. It is possible that speculation concerning a muscle sense may have taken place prior to this date. However, it is likely that the complete acceptance of Aristotle's doctrine of the five senses was far more probable prior to Descartes. It may not be exaggerating to say that the treatment of Aristotle's doctrine of the senses as axiomatic may have actively hindered interest in proprioception and significantly delayed its investigation.

The nineteenth century saw the gradual emergence of interest by physiologists in the muscular sense. In 1812 the French physiologist Bichat opened the way for physiologists by speculating on the presence of sensitivity in muscles. It remained, however, for Charles Bell (1826) to provide a physiological interpretation of the mechanisms by which this muscle sensitivity might operate. In his paper, 'On the Nervous Circle which Connects the Voluntary Muscles with the Brain', Bell outlined what today would be called a simple feedback mechanism. He conceived of commands being carried from the brain to the muscles and reports on the condition of the muscles being transmitted in the reverse direction. Bell's contribution has often been labelled as the beginning of scientific interest in proprioception.

Bell did not describe his system in histological terms and it was some years before the muscle receptors were identified. There is still some doubt over the identity of the discoverers of the muscle spindles. Ruffini (1898) suggested that the discovery was made by Hassal in 1851, but that the first reliable histological account did not appear until 1861, being produced by Wiesman. Boring (1942) attributed the discovery to Kühne in 1863, claiming that it was Kühne who provided the detailed description and also named the receptors muscle spindles.

Whichever of these is correct, the mere statement of the discovery does little to convey the controversy with which these advances were greeted. It is a fairly straightforward matter to trace a growing accuracy in the analysis of proprioception. Following only the thread of development which, with hindsight, has proven to be correct ignores the contentious nature of the discovery. For example, Wiesman, although attributed with a first accurate description of the spindles, was completely incorrect in his speculation concerning their function. Both he and Kühne were convinced that the muscle spindles were centres for muscular regeneration.

Similarly, there was distinct disagreement among the growing numbers of psychologists as to the means by which the body appreciated or was aware of its own movement. Physiological psychology, as an independent discipline, was a phenomenon still some decades in the future. Towards the end of the nineteenth century members of the influential school of psychology loosely termed the Introspectionists had outlined a totally different view as an alternative to the belief in muscular sensitivity as a source of awareness of bodily activity. The Wundtian school of introspectionists was particularly inclined to believe that 'mental motive energy' or 'locomotive faculty' is the principal channel through which movement is appreciated. Their suggestion was that the sensations of movement come from consciousness of the amount of nervous energy transmitted from the brain in order to make the movement, rather than a reception of information from the muscle itself. This divergent view, largely forgotten today, was a central issue at the time and not simply a peripheral statement of psychological theory.

Parenthetically, it may be noted that the concept of locomotive faculty was resuscitated by Lashley (1917) in a new guise. With the label 'motor outflow information' or 'active movement kinaesthesis', the concept of perceptually registered motor commands has been shown to account for the accuracy of some kinds of movement. Although there has been little research into this aspect of proprioception since Lashley's experiments, he demonstrated that for a well practised movement loss of afference from proprioceptors of the leg does not result in a loss of accuracy in that movement, provided that the leg is not loaded or movement otherwise resisted. Several modern authorities (e.g. see Howard, 1966) suggest that ballistic movements may be monitored by means of motor outflow information since transmission time for proprioceptive impulses precludes the possibility of control on the basis of feedback. Merton (1964) postulated that most active movement is controlled in this way.

It was not until the decade 1895-1905, however, that the original controversy was resolved with the advent of reflexology. This development in physiology, which was to affect the course of psychological history profoundly, was presaged by Sherrington's (1894) experiments on the degeneration of nervous fibres following sectioning. By tracing the degeneration of 'muscle sense' fibres to their dorsal roots, Sherrington finally established their sensory nature. These findings and the subsequent establishment of reflex arcs contributed to the demise of introspectionist beliefs. In 1910 Wundt, however, still clung to a modified concept of 'locomotive faculty', some four years after Sherrington's paper.

Thus far the discussion has tended to illustrate the history of research into proprioception by reference to the discovery of the physiological basis of the 'muscle sense'. This is justified by the fact that it was this aspect of proprioception which commanded most attention during the nineteenth century; other aspects were developing simultaneously however. For example, a large proportion of the earliest work in psychophysics involved experimentation in the field of proprioception. Weber, working in the 1840's, came to his conclusions concerning the detection of differences in sensory stimulation using proprioceptive judgements initially. Emphasis in the study of psychophysics was soon to shift to other modalities, but the contribution of proprioception was significant.

In a similar way, although the attention of psychologists was drawn to discoveries of the muscle sense, other receptor systems labelled as proprioceptors by Sherrington were also being discovered during the nineteenth century. In 1840 Pacini discovered corpuscles in deep subcutaneous tissue. These corpuscles were named after him, although it is probable that they had been identified as early as 1741 by Vater and the discovery forgotten for almost a century. There was again a delay before the function of the corpuscles was correctly assessed. In 1867 Rauber demonstrated that the Pacinian corpuscles are also related to ligaments and tendons and hypothesised their role in the transmission of information concerning joint position and movement. The receptor organs in the tendon were discovered by Rollett in 1876, but Golgi provided a complete description in 1880, produced evidence for their function and gave them his name.

In looking at the history of research into the proprioceptors of the inner ear, it is again all too easy to forget what an astonishing discovery this must have been. Superficially, it is difficult to think of a more unlikely place for a balance organ than inside the hearing mechanism. Yet with hindsight the details of the discovery are robbed of their surprise.

Attention appears to have been given to the vestibular mechanisms first by Purkinje who, in the period 1820-1825, described giddiness and dizziness as being related to the mechanisms of the inner ear. This work stimulated the psychological investigations in this area and Flourens, experimenting between 1824 and 1830, demonstrated that lesions of the semicircular canals cause muscular incoordination in the plane of the effected canals. Later in the century more precise details became available concerning the function of the canals through the work of three independent scientists. Mach (1875), Breuer (1874), and Crum Brown (1875) all outlined a conception of the action of the canals which stressed the importance of movements of the endolymph and therefore became known as the hydrodynamic theory of canal function.

Towards the end of the nineteenth century, therefore, the separate elements of what Sherrington called proprioception were already discovered; nor was he the first to see some kind of unity encompassing the diverse movement receptors. Bastian proposed that the term 'muscle sense' be replaced by kinaesthesis as early as 1880. The term was taken up by Goldsheider in 1889. He proposed the now familiar threefold classification of kinaesthesis into muscular, tendonous and articular sensitivity.

The anatomical structure and many aspects of the physiological function were known, at least in gross detail, by the early part of this century. It was not until the advent of sophisticated electronic amplifying and recording devices that the next major stage in the growing knowledge of proprioceptive function was achieved. The status of research findings in modern physiological terms will be dealt with in Chapter 2.

A question of definition

In this short review of evolving interest in proprioception during the nineteenth century, it may be noted that there was relatively little disagreement over the definition of the terms at that time. Dissent became evident with Sherrington's invention of the term proprioception. Following 1906, there was a tendency for physiologists to use Sherrington's classification, whereas many psychologists continued to use kinaesthesis to denote the same phenomenon or at least that part excluding the vestibular apparatus. Problems of definition were relatively unimportant in the early part of this century since it was merely a question of choosing one of two labels. Sherrington's 'proprioception' was accepted to mean muscular, tendonous, joint and vestibular receptors, whereas Goldscheider's definition of kinaesthesis included only the first three of these systems.

Both terms were however, originally generic, since both terms included several different types of receptors, all of which served to provide some information concerning a vaguely designated sense of movement. This generic quality has been viewed by many as a disadvantage, and (since Sherrington's time) attempts have been made to create a more precise definition. Many of these revisions have differentially emphasized certain aspects of the original and the result has been a mounting confusion over the precise meaning of the terms during the last decades.

A further exacerbating factor has been the enormous increase in anatomical and physiological knowledge since Sherrington's time. It is now even more apparent that included within the terms proprioception and kinaesthesis are receptor systems with very different structures and functional properties. For example, Merton (1964) reviewed evidence regarding the degree to which different receptors included in the term proprioception might subserve perception: finding that many distinctions existed in the relative perceptual contributions of these receptors, Merton saw little value in maintaining use of the term and suggested that it be abandoned.

Similar points have been made concerning kinaesthesis. At one extreme the terms proprioception and kinaesthesis have been used as synonyms: thus Howard and Templeton (1966) defined kinaesthesis at one point as 'The discrimination of the positions and movements of body parts based on information other than visual, auditory or verbal'. (pp. 72). According to this somewhat negative approach, kinaesthesis appears equivalent to Sherrington's proprioception since it does not exclude the vestibular apparatus. Howard and Templeton, however, did make a distinction in practical terms, dealing in one chapter with 'Kinaesthesis' and in another with 'The Vestibular Apparatus'.

At the other extreme, Smith (1969) viewed the definition of kinaesthesis in a similar way to the position taken by Merton (1964) concerning proprioception. Smith divided the original concept of kinaesthesis into those components which may subserve perception and those which do not. Part of her rationale for this is the Greek derivation of the term (kinesis = motion and aesthesia=to perceive). At one point, Smith said that '. . . kinesthesis implies the possibility of conscious recognition.' (pp. 33). On this basis Smith included in her discussion of kinaesthesis only the joint receptor systems and, without definition, called muscle and tendonous receptors proprioceptors. A similar, although less extreme suggestion, was made by Henry (1953) who saw a need for distinguishing two types of kinaesthetic receptors—conscious and unconscious.

Bearing in mind Smith's emphasis on the perceptual factors in kinaesthesis, it is rather strange that she also decided to call kinaesthesis a 'sensory modality'. Having exactly the same regard for a distinction between perceptual and non-perceptual systems, Gibson (1966) came to a very different conclusion. Like Smith, Gibson suggested that kinaesthesis is concerned with movement and its conscious appreciation. Gibson found it obvious therefore that vision must be included in some way in kinaesthesis since we can visually monitor movement. Gibson was also conscious of the varied sources of information included in the term and he therefore spoke of many different kinds of kinaesthesis: articular kinaesthesis; vestibular kinaesthesis; cutaneous kinaesthesis; and visual kinaesthesis. His conclusion was that, 'Kinesthesis . . . is one of the best examples of detection without a special modality of sensation' (Gibson 1966, pp. 111).

Gibson made the same point concerning proprioception. He noted that it is probable that the doctrine of 'specific nerve energies' held earlier this century has blinded later researchers to the fact that movement sensitivity does not depend on specialized receptors. It is not simply a sixth sense to be added to Aristotle's five classical senses. On this basis Gibson made a new division of proprioception. At one level he suggested there is the 'Lower Proprioceptive systems: Posture and Equilibrium' and at another 'The Higher Proprioceptive systems: purposive action'. This latter category is subdivided in the same way in which kinaesthesis is divided, that is, into articular proprioception, vestibular proprioception, cutaneous proprioception, visual proprioception, and also includes one factor missing in kinaesthesis, auditory proprioception (the registering of sounds made by action). Any distinction between proprioception and kinaesthesis is left unexplained. At one point (pp. 111) Gibson noted that 'Kinesthesis . . . is almost the same thing as proprioception'; the only overt difference is that auditory functions are included in one list and not in the other. Apparently dissatisfied with this type of breakdown, Gibson proposed a new term: the Haptic system. The Haptic system is defined by Gibson as '. . . an apparatus by which the individual gets information about both the environment and his body . . . It is the perceptual system by which animals and even man are literally in touch with the environment'. (pp. 97) In his chapter on the Haptic system Gibson treated muscle sensitivity, joint sensitivity, and the contribution of the vestibular system as well as various forms of cutaneous sensitivity. The Haptic system therefore parallels most aspects of proprioception, the distinction being that Gibson treated the perceptual process very much more extensively than the sensory aspects. It is also clear that Gibson did not equate proprioception completely with the Haptic system, for, although he mentioned visual proprioception, he did not include this aspect in his discussion of the Haptic system.

As a sample of the current semantic controversy over kinaesthesis and proprioception, these examples may give some indication of the ambivalent position in which any reviewer finds himself. Not only is there disagreement concerning the definition of proprioception, there is even disagreement over whether proprioception may be viewed as a sensory modality. In other words, problems exist concerning the content of a review and even whether it is justified to treat proprioception as a phenomenon with any unifying qualities. It is equally probable that any new definition may serve only to create further confusion.

Whilst acknowledging the validity of much of Gibson's work concerning the perceptual integration of sensory information, it is felt that it is justifiable to examine the contribution of one (albeit diverse) set of sensory sources.

The traditional proprioceptors have a degree of unity in the sense that they all have various kinds of body movement as their adequate stimulus.

Although there is an interaction between and an integration of the information derived from proprioceptors and information from other sensory systems, this applies in varying degrees to all sensory modalities. For example, sensory-tonic field theory has at its foundation this type of interaction between sensory sources of information (e.g. see Wapner, Werner and Chandler, 1951). Thus, just as vision may interact with tactual cues to produce perceptions, so proprioceptors interact with information from other sources. This does not make invalid the study of vision or the visual contribution alone. Similarly the contributions of proprioceptors may be examined with justification both independently and in terms of their interaction with other information. Also, an exclusion of certain types of proprioceptors because of their lack of direct cortical links [following Merton (1964) and Smith (1969)] seems a somewhat arbitrary decision for two reasons. Firstly, at a practical level, a division precludes the possibility of achieving completeness in the review which may be achieved by examining both sets of receptors. The contribution of all systems, whether at a conscious or unconscious level, may be assessed. Secondly, at a physiological level, the absence of a direct link from receptors to the cortex may not necessarily preclude some indirect participation in perception. Even if this is speculative, it is quite probable that receptors without direct cortical connections do play a major role in the unconscious control of muscular activity.

For these reasons a negatively biased definition has been selected, similar to that proposed by Howard and Templeton (1966) concerning kinaesthesis. Proprioception is to be defined as the appreciation of movement and position of the body and parts of the body based on information from other than visual, auditory or superficial cutaneous sources. Viewed from a positive point of view, proprioception is therefore defined in a way very similar to the original conception of the term by Sherrington.

2

PHYSIOLOGICAL BASES OF PROPRIOCEPTION

Chapter

2 PHYSIOLOGICAL BASES OF PROPRIOCEPTION

Introduction

In the first chapter much of the material normally included in an introduction to the physiology of proprioception was discussed. This chapter deals with an examination of the modern findings in the area. During the late 1920's and early 1930's the discovery of electronic amplifying and recording devices opened a new dimension of physiological research. The pioneer work in proprioception was carried out by Adrian & Zotterman (1926) and Matthews (1931, 1933). Adrian developed the technique of recording from single sensory nerve endings. Matthews, however, applied the technique to recording from muscle spindles in frogs and mammals. It was in Matthews' early papers that the basic responses of the muscle spindle to stretch and contraction were described. Although Matthews provided evidence for the functions of muscle spindles, his results had been predicted in a speculative paper by Fulton and Pi-Suner (1928). Matthews' experiments also provided detailed information concerning the function of the Golgi tendon organs. Since the 1930's continuing sophistication of electronic recording devices has enabled more accurate descriptions and further discoveries of physiological functions. This chapter will be mainly concerned with these later findings.

One cautionary note mut be extended. This is not a physiology textbook and a complete account of the anatomy and physiology of proprioceptive systems would be out of place. Consequently more detailed accounts are referenced at appropriate points. Despite the review nature of this chapter, however, it is felt that consideration of the physiological bases is essential for an understanding of later sections.

The Muscle Spindles

For a full account of the muscle spindles the most detailed description was provided by Barker (1948). Matthews (1964) considered the more modern findings.

The muscle spindle receptors are located in the ordinary or extrafusal muscle fibres. The spindle is formed of between two and ten intrafusal muscle fibres which may be thought of as a single functional unit. The muscle spindle is essentially a specialized form of muscle fibre and it contains contractile elements as well as the receptor organs. Each intrafusal muscle fibre is distinguished by three major sections; the contractile elements are located proximally and distally in the so-called polar regions and between these sections lies the equatorial region. The equatorial region is itself separated into three sub-sections. In the centre lies a nuclear bag, which is a slight swelling of the fibre containing a lymph filled capsule. The nuclear bag is separated from the polar regions by the myotube or transitional section. The nuclear bag contains receptor end-organs and the lymph serves as a protection from mechanical pressures. This ensures that the stimulus for the end organs is changes of tension along their length. (See Fig. 1)

The endings found in the nuclear bag are known as primary endings. Secondary endings are found in the myotube region. Sometimes these endings are referred to as annulo-spiral endings and flower spray endings respectively. In man, however, the endings are not distinguishable by shape and are usually identified by their location. Both sets of endings respond to the stretching of the muscle in which they are found. There are, however, some slight functional differences between the two sets of endings. These differences are probably due to differences in location; the secondary endings are found in myotube sections which have some contractile elements, whereas the primary endings are found within the nuclear bag (Granit, 1955). Spindle firing is elicited during many kinds of stretch, the primary endings apparently having a very much lower threshold than the secondary. The primary endings also show a low frequency resting discharge. During linear stretch the primary endings increase their rate of discharge markedly whereas the discharge of the secondary endings increases little above the level found in maintained stretch (Cooper 1961). Perhaps the most distinct difference between the patterns of firing of the two sets of endings is found in their reaction to the release of stretch. The primary endings cease firing immediately, but the secondary endings maintain a low level of discharge during the release phase. This phenomenon is further demonstrated in the responses to sinusoidal stretch where a fairly regular pattern of discharge is found in the secondary endings. The wave formation of sinusoidal stretch is reflected to a much greater extent in cycles of primary spindle firing (Matthews 1964).

Muscle spindles are arranged 'in parallel' with the extrafusal muscle fibres. When the extrafusal muscle contracts the muscle spindle receptors cease firing. This pause in the discharge from the muscle spindle receptors occurs particularly in isotonic contraction and it continues until contraction of the intrafusal muscle fibre realigns the spindle in terms of length with the extrafusal muscle fibres surrounding it. Usually there is also a pause in

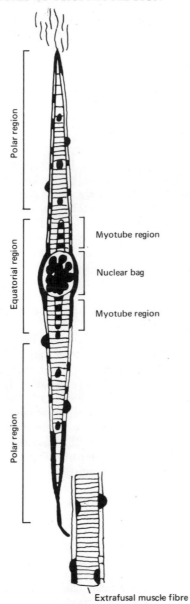

Fig. 1. Diagram of a single intrafusal muscle fibre; each polar region has been shortened to about a third of its typical length. The width has been increased by about one half. (Adapted from Barker 1948 Quarterly Journal of Microscopical Science, 89.)

isometric contraction due to the take up of elasticity in the muscles and tendons releasing tension on the muscle spindle. If isometric contraction continues after the initial realignment of spindle and extrafusal fibre has occurred, the spindle firing will continue (see Howard and Templeton 1966, for a summary).

Adaptation is rapid for the muscle spindles and for this reason the maximum discharge depends not only on the amount of tension applied but also on the rate with which stretch occurs. Ignoring the effects of adaptation, the discharge from the spindles is approximately proportional to the logarithm of the load (Howard 1966).

Afferents from the spindles feed into the dorsal roots of the spinal cord. Here they project up the spinal cord to the cerebellum. Mountcastle (1957) has demonstrated that stimulation of the muscle spindles does not produce any response in the somaesthetic area of the cortex and it is therefore considered unlikely that there is a direct link from the muscle spindles to levels higher than the cerebellum. The muscle spindle afferents are also involved in monosynaptic reflexes. These are the simplest form of sensory-motor relationship. The axon from the dorsal root terminates directly on the second neuron of the feedback loop, the ventral horn motor cell. This reflexive function of muscle spindle afferents is relatively uncommon in higher animals, only forming part of the postural mechanisms and influencing the maintenance of body tonus.

Apart from this simple feedback loop involved in reflexive control, there is a further feedback loop of which the muscle spindle afferents form a part. This has become known as the gamma efferent feedback loop. (The terms gamma and alpha fibres are based on a classificatory system of Erlanger and Gasser 1937, relying on conduction velocities.) The muscle spindles are innervated by gamma fibres, whose efferent discharge causes contraction in the polar regions of the intrafusal muscle fibres. The result is a change in tension in the equatorial region of the fibre and therefore an alteration in afferent activity. The afferent activity in turn affects the alpha neurons which stimulate contraction of the extrafusal muscle.

Eldred, Granit and Merton (1953), on the basis of this evidence, suggested two entirely different ways for contraction of the extrafusal muscles to occur. Firstly, contraction may occur as a result of direct alpha stimulation or secondly, through the gamma fibre system. These authors pointed out that the initiation of contraction via the gamma system has the advantage of higher levels of feedback control, but this may produce delays in contraction because of conduction time. They concluded that, 'The exact conditions under which . . . pathways become dominant remain to be determined'. Howard and Templeton (1966) speculated that the direct pathway (i.e. alpha stimulation) may be used for 'ballistic' or well-practiced movements and that the indirect pathway may be reserved for exploratory or tentative movements.

A complete analysis of the gamma fibre feedback loop is not yet developed and there is still some controversy concerning the role of this system. It is apparent that the feedback loop is mediated through the anterior lobe of the cerebellum and the diencephallic reticular formation. The loop is, however, very complex. Each muscle spindle receives several gamma efferents and each gamma efferent has branches to several spindles. The role of the system in voluntary activity within the intact animal may, because of this complexity, take some time to elucidate, if indeed it can be experimentally analysed.

One further aspect of this complexity is illustrated by a phenomenon demonstrated by Gellhorn (1948) and Breinin (1957). They found a feedback influence not only upon the extrafusal muscle in which the spindle is found, but also upon that muscle's antagonist. Their results differed in terms of the form of this influence and to date no generalized conclusion has been reached.

It is apparent that muscle spindles operate at two distinct levels. At one level they are concerned with providing information concerning stretch occuring within the muscle. At another level they participate in a feedback system involving contraction. Grossman (1967) suggested that the latter function may often be dominant and even override the normal suppression of spindle activity which occurs during the contraction of the extrafusal muscle.

The Golgi Tendon Organs

The Golgi tendon organs are typically found at the insertion of the tendons into the muscle. According to Barker (1948), it is also probable that there are frequently Golgi tendon organs at the insertion of the muscle spindles themselves. This causes some methodological difficulties in that production of a spindle preparation without interference from tendon organs is difficult (see Granit 1955).

The functioning of the Golgi tendon organs is similar to that of the muscle spindle receptors and the two systems co-operate closely. There are, however, some important differences in the functional properties of these systems. The Golgi tendon organs are responsive to the degree of tension within the muscle, but they are responsive to the total tension whether this is produced by stretch or by contraction. Tendon organs therefore discharge during that period of time during contraction when the spindles cease firing. For illustrative purposes therefore, it is often suggested that whereas the muscle spindles appear to function in 'parallel' with the extrafusal muscle, the Golgi tendon organs operate as though they were in 'series' with the muscle. The Golgi tendon organs show no resting discharge and generally have a much higher threshold to tension than the muscle spindle receptors. The tendon organs also appear to adapt less rapidly. For this reason, in terms of total transmission from the muscle, the proportion of discharge is greatest from the muscle spindles at low levels of tension produced by stretch, but this proportion decreases as the tension increases and the proportion of contribution of the tendon organs increases.

The afferent pathways from the tendon organs are similar to the afferents from the muscle spindles. They enter the spinal cord by way of the dorsal roots and there initiate monosynaptic reflexes. Whereas the muscle spindles initiate stretch reflexes the tendon organs are concerned in the production of inhibitory reflexes. In a long series of experiments on reflexive behaviour, Granit and co-workers (see Granit (1955) for a summary) demonstrated that the action of the spindles serves to facilitate the contraction of the muscle within which they are found, but to inhibit that muscle's antagonist. The Golgi tendon organs, on the other hand, were found to inhibit the muscle upon the tendon of which they were located and to facilitate the action of the muscle's antagonist. Apparently because of the higher thresholds of the tendon organs, inhibition does not appear until higher levels of stretch are achieved. With severe distortion of the limb the inhibition effect may override facilitation causing sudden lengthening in the extrafusal muscle. In simplified form the system appears to work in the following way. Passive stretch causes reflex facilitation of the contraction of the muscle. This is mediated through the muscle spindle afferents. With increasing tension the higher threshold tendon organs begin to discharge causing reflexive inhibition of the contraction. If the distortion of the muscle continues this inhibition of contraction may become dominant and a 'clasp knife reflex' or sudden lengthening occur.

The tendon organ afferents also project up the spinal cord to the cerebellum. There does not appear to be a direct link to the cortex (Oscarsson 1966). Also, it is thought unlikely (Hunt and Paintal 1958) that the tendon receptors directly affect the gamma efferent system.

Apart from the role of the tendon organs in reflex control of muscles, therefore, it seems most probable that their contribution to total proprioceptive information is restricted to providing additional monitoring of tension changes which are recorded and integrated with other sensory information at the cerebellar level.

The Joint Receptors

Contained within the joints are three distinct forms of receptors. These receptors being isolated from the muscles are not sensitive to changes in muscular tension. Their stimulus appears to be movement around the joint and joint position. There are, however, differences between the three types of receptor in functional terms. Located within the ligaments, which bind the joint and limit its movement, are found endings similar to the Golgi tendon organs. The receptors in the ligament are therefore known as Golgi-type endings or free endings. Within the joint capsule itself, particularly in the connective tissue, the receptors are known as spray-type endings (sometimes called Ruffini-type endings because of their similarity to the receptors in the skin). Also found within the joint capsule are receptors termed pacinian or paciniform corpuscles. There is still some doubt concerning the precise function of all the receptors of the joint although some informed speculation has been possible. To a large extent the evidence seems to point to a distinction between those receptors signalling position and those receptors which provide information concerning movement (Gardner 1950, Boyd, 1954).

The spray-endings and the Golgi-type endings appear to signal position, whereas the pacinian corpuscles register movement. The position receptors have an extraordinary flexibility of discharge. They are generally speaking slowly adapting and appear to discharge at specific joint angles without reference to the direction of movement. A single receptor may adapt at different rates for different joint angles and there may be differences in the range over which receptors are sensitive. That is, some receptors may fire at any joint angle, others may be most active for small joint angles and others at large joint angles (Berry, Karl and Hinsey, 1950).

It is also worth noting that although cutaneous receptors are not included within the definition of proprioceptors, Adrian, Cottell and Hoagland (1931) demonstrated that cutaneous receptors show a discharge in response to skin deformations and it is likely that changes in the firing pattern of the skin receptors may therefore provide additional information concerning the movement of limbs.

The pacinian corpuscles produce very different discharge patterns. These movement receptors adapt very rapidly and their response is independent of joint angle. These receptors have as their stimuli the velocity, acceleration and direction of limb movement. Thus some receptors may respond only to a specific direction of movement. For other receptors there are likely to be quantitative changes in frequency of discharge dependent upon the velocity of movement (See Smith 1969 for a summary).

There is also a possibility that 'intermediate' receptors may exist. Wiersma (1963) noted that within some species there is probably a continuum of receptors in the joints from those whose responding is completely limited to signalling position, through those receptors whose responding is dependent upon both position and movement to those solely responsible for signalling movement.

The afferents from the joint receptors project via the dorsal root into the lemniscal system, the thalamus and so to the sensory cortex. The specific route of the afferent fibres of joint receptors is fairly straightforward. From the dorsal root the fibres form part of the dorsal funiculi. At the level of the brainstem they synapse within the nuclei cuneatus and gracilis. The secondary neurons form part of the medial lemniscal system. A second synapse occurs in the thalamus and the third stage or tertiary neurons project to the sensorimotor cortex. At the level of the thalamus, Mountcastle, Poggio and Werner (1963) noted a high degree of neural integration and convergence. This suggests that there is probably a summarising and encoding process occurring at this level. Perception of movement characteristics, therefore, may be based on less than direct information from the receptors. However, it has been demonstrated, (Mountcastle, 1957) that mechanical stimulation of single receptors does produce a response in the cortex, and similarly, cortical responding is found from electrical stimulation of the joint afferents (Gardner and Haddad, 1953).

Since the afferents from joints participate in perception it may be worth observing at this point some factors influencing perception, although this topic must be dealt with at a later stage in greater detail. Perception involves the active participation of the individual in his interpretation of the stimuli received. Thus, temporary states of the organism, e.g. fatigue, drugs, etc. are likely to change perception even though the physical characteristics of the afferent input may be the same. Also, the way in which information from the receptors is organized and interpreted will depend on previous experience and familiarity with the movements in question. Perhaps of even greater importance is the question of attention. The same individual may perceive or fail to perceive identical stimuli on two different occasions because of attention or inattention at these times. It is clear therefore, that generalizations concerning the nature of perception of movement are impossible on the basis of the type of afferent nerve impulses. For this reason, the question of perception may be better discussed in the light of behavioural rather than physiological evidence.

The Vestibular System.

Wendt (1951) and Howard and Templeton, (1966) both provided extensive summaries of the function of the vestibular mechanisms. Situated within the inner ear are sense organs known collectively as the vestibular apparatus or labyrinth. It is usual for a distinction to be made between two types of vestibular organ, the vestibular or semicircular canals and the utricles. Whilst this distinction is justified on anatomical grounds, differences between the canals and the utricles is less evident functionally. It has generally been assumed that the canals monitor movement of the head and that the utricles register static head position. Jongkees and Groen (1946) first pointed out the fallacy of this distinction. Although the most obvious stimulus to the utricles is gravity, they are nevertheless sensitive to all forms of linear acceleration. Similarly, since the canals form a three part system, the integration of information from all canals can provide information concerning the direction of rotary head movement as well as accelerative information.

The Vestibular Canals

Anatomically, the three vestibular canals lie approximately at right angles to each other in man. The canals are usually identified as horizontal, superior and posterior. In vivo, with man standing upright, the horizontal canal forms an angle of 30° to the horizontal, the superior canal is vertical and makes approximately a 55° angle to the frontal plane and the posterior canal which is also vertical makes a 45° angle to the frontal plane. Each of the canals is effectively an autonomous fluid circuit, belying its semicircular label. The canals meet at a sac known as the utricle, the second of the sensory organs (See Fig. 2).

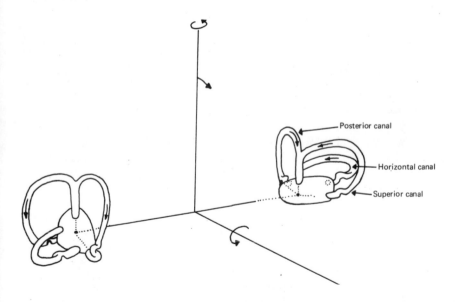

Fig. 2. The arrangement of the vestibular canals on each side of the head. (Adapted from Groen. The problem of the spinning top applied to the semi-circular canals. Confin)

The sensory end-organs within the canals are located within a slight bulge in the canal situated close to the canal's junction with the utricle. These end organs take the form of a sensory epithelium or crista ampullaris. This epithelium consists of a ridge containing many multiciliated sensory cells. The cilia arising in the epithelium are all embedded in a gelatinous mass called the cupula. The cupula moves as though hinged and since the opposite wall of the canal is symmetrically arched the cupula prevents any movement of the endolymph contained within the canals past that point (See Fig. 3).

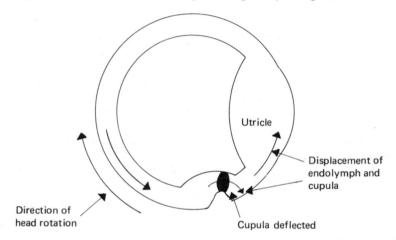

Fig. 3. Schematic diagram of a vestibular canal showing the complete fluid circuit. The arrows depict the consequence of a clockwise rotation of the head in the plane of the canal. (Howard and Templeton, Human Spatial Orientation. Copyright © 1966 John Wiley & Sons Ltd. By permission of John Wiley & Sons, Ltd.)

When the cupula moves the cristae discharge. That is, when the canals move relative to the endolymph, movement of the cupula occurs causing discharge from the cristae. Thus discharge occurs following any rotary movements of the head which occur within the plane of a specific canal. If rotation is maintained at a constant angular velocity, the fluid endolymph 'catches up' with the canal due to friction between the endolymph and the canal wall causing the cupula to return to its resting position. When this happens the cristae cease to discharge. If angular rotation is suddenly stopped after a prolonged period of rotation then the cupula will be deflected in the opposite direction, again causing discharge in the cristae. Since the cupula takes time to return to the resting position, the behavioural effects are similar to a deceleration process. However, if the duration of rotation is short, the effects of acceleration and deceleration are counter-balanced and no after effects occur.

No precise conclusion has yet been reached concerning the properties of the cristae or the individual sensory cells located in the epithelium. Most of the sensory cells are bidirectional, that is, they respond to movement of the cupula in either direction. There is, however, some evidence of differentiation of function between the cells (Gernandt, 1949).

The Utricles

The utricle is found at the point where the three canals meet. This sac is filled with endolymph and the sensory mechanism or macula is located on the anterior and medial walls of the utricular cavity. The macula is similar in nature to the sensory organs of the canals consisting of an epithelium of ciliated sensory cells. The cilia project into a gelatinous mass which contains particles of calcium carbonate called the otoliths. The utricular cavity is filled with endolymph, but the otoliths are much heavier than the endolymph and move in response to linear acceleration of the head. This movement of the otoliths is thought to stimulate the hair cells or cilia. The precise nature of the adequate stimulus of the hair cells has not been fully established.

An extreme interpretation of recent evidence is made by Wing (1963) who suggested that the utricle is largely vestigial in mammals and information derived from other modalities is more important in fulfilling the traditionally ascribed role of the utricle in maintaining balance. It is certainly true that in man the function of the vestibular organs may be taken over by other modalities. Where removal of one or both of the vestibular mechanisms becomes necessary because of disease it is possible for retraining to produce a close approximation to normal balance (Cooksey 1946). It appears from this evidence that the other senses may compensate for a lack of vestibular information. However, if the capacity of the other senses is restricted in some way, the absence of the vestibular mechanisms may cause more serious defects in the maintenance of balance. For example, after retraining it may be possible for man to rely on vision and the other proprioceptive sources and produce normal gait and equilibration in the absence of the vestibular mechanisms. If the quality of the visual environment is reduced however, by lowering illumination, performance may be disrupted. Although Wing's interpretation may be justified therefore to some extent, it is clear that under certain conditions, in the dark for example, the role of utricular information may be important.

The afferent pathways of the vestibular system are highly complex. Axons from the vestibular apparatus form a part of the eighth or auditory nerve and project to the brainstem in close association with the cochlear branch and enter the medulla. Many of the fibres terminate in the four vestibular nuclei of the brainstem. These are designated as the medial, lateral, superior, and spinal nuclei and all receive terminating axons. They are also the source for important ascending and descending fibres. The majority of the projections from the vestibular nuclei are involved in the mediation of vestibulo related reflexes. Thus one set of fibres originating in the spinal nucleus descends the spinal column in the so-called lateral vestibulo spinal tract, terminating in the motor neuron pools. Similarly there are descending fibres from the medial, lateral as well as spinal nuclei which pass via the medial vestibulospinal tract and terminate in motor neuron pools. Both these sets of fibres are thought to mediate vestibulospinal reflexes. There are also fibres which pass from the nuclei to the oculomotor centres of the brainstem and produce the vestibular nystagmus reflex. A direct pathway leads from the vestibular nuclei to various parts of the cerebellum. The vestibuloreticular pathways from the superior and medial nuclei distribute widely throughout the bulbar and pontine reticular formation. Most recently it has been found that there are also projections from the vestibular nuclei to the cerebral cortex. There is a distribution of fibres to some thalamic nuclei and from there to the superior temporal lobe and pre-motor areas of the frontal lobe (Gernandt 1964).

Functionally therefore, the vestibular mechanisms serve several different roles. No doubt their principal phylogenetic task has been in the production of body righting reflexes. Despite the fact that decerebrate preparations show that these functions are still present among higher organisms, it is clear that the information derived from other sources constitutes a more effective form of control in the intact organism. It is true that the influence of vestibular reflex control may be demonstrated in human neonates, but the development of voluntary control soon supercedes this reflexive activity.

The vestibular apparatus also contributes at two other levels. Firstly, there is the integration of vestibular information with information from other systems operating at an unconscious level, e.g. the muscular and tendon afferent sources. Secondly, there is the contribution of the vestibular mechanisms to the total perception of movement, achieved via the connection of the vestibular apparatus to the cortex.

The.Cerebellum

It has been noted that many of the proprioceptive feedback loops involve the participation of the cerebellum. The muscle spindles, the tendon organs and the vestibular mechanisms all have direct connection with this organ. It is necessary therefore that an examination be made of the cerebellum's role within the context of these feedback loops and the totality of proprioceptive feedback control.

The cerebellum lies inferior to the occipital lobe of the cerebrum. It is bounded ventrally by the brainstem although extending laterally beyond it.

The cerebellum consists of four nuclei surrounded by white matter. These nuclei are known as the fastigial, globose, emboliform and dentate nuclei. Surrounding the white matter is a convoluted cortex whose surface is formed into parallel folds or folia. A large central longitudinal fold known as the vermis divides the cerebellum into two hemispheres. There are also two ventral projections from the posterior cerebellum called flocculi. (See Ruch-Patton 1965, and Ruch 1951 for excellent anatomical and physiological descriptions). Several deep fissures within the cortex demarcate lobes. These divisions on anatomical grounds do not, however, represent autonomous physiological areas and they are of relatively little significance. As a functional basis the essential components of the cerebellum are as follows. The flocculonodular lobe, separated from the body of the cerebellum by the fissura posterolateralis, is one fuctionally distinct section. The body of the cerebellum or corpus cerebelli may be divided into an anterior and posterior lobe, by means of the fissura prima. Sometimes a functional distinction is drawn between two sections of the posterior lobe divided by the fissura prepyramidalis (See Fig. 4).

Traditionally the cerebellum has been ascribed the role of coordinating centre for motor responses. Particularly, the cerebellum was thought to govern 'automatic' responses. However there is growing evidence of the influence of the cerebellum on all forms of voluntary as well as automatic movements. By far the major contribution to knowledge of cerebellar function has come from experiments on infrahuman organisms, and since there have been known phylogenetic changes in the function and levels of participation of the cerebellum, some caution needs to be exerted in generalizing results of these experiments to man. There are, nonetheless, relevant data concerning the function of the various cerebellar areas and these may be summarized in the following ways.

Ablation studies have shown that complete loss of the cerebellum does not result in an inability to move, nor in the loss of capacity to perform a particular motor task. Rather it is the quality of the movement which is changed. Smoothness, accuracy and coordination are apparently no longer possible once the cerebellar function in the feedback loops is diminished. There is also a noticeable increase in abnormalities in muscle tonus and a general disorientation. of movement. It has been shown however, that a compensatory process can occur after ablation. That is, the severity of movement abnormalities may be reduced with time although a complete recovery of normal motor functioning is not possible.

Selective damage to the cerebellum may cause specific types of motor malfunctioning. For example, damage in the region of the flocculi, which receive vestibular afferents can result in a loss of equilibratory capacity. Lesions of the cerebellar hemispheres may produce a generalized atonia or tremor. The hemispheres are also organized somatotopically. (This soma-

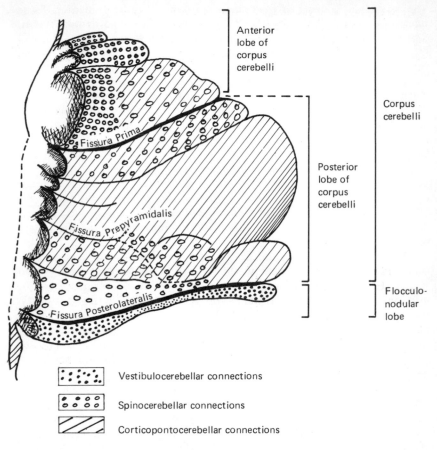

Fig. 4. Highly schematic diagram of the mammalian cerebellum showing cerebellar connections. The shaded area at the left represents a cut through the middle of the vermis to show the depth of the fissures. (Dow, 1942. Reprinted from Biological Reviews. Vol. 17, 179-220 by permission of Cambridge University Press.)

totopic organization is not as marked in the cerebellum as in the cerebral cortex). For this reason, lesions within the cerebellar hemispheres are likely to cause disorders of voluntary movement specific to the area destroyed. Similarly, since the cortex of the hemispheres receives afferents from the nuclei, destruction of a nucleus or nuclei will result in equivalent effects on motor responding as lesions of the related area of the cerebellar cortex (see Grossman, 1967).

Ruch (1965), has summarised the function of the cerebellum. Firstly the cerebellum receives afferents from all other sensory modalities as well as proprioceptive and vestibular afferents. The anterior lobe is reciprocally connected with somatosensory area I of the cerebral cortex. The posterior lobe is reciprocally connected with somatosensory area II. The motor area of the cerebral cortex and the anterior lobe are also reciprocally connected.

The cerebellum is therefore ideally placed for coordinating information arising both from the exteroceptors and proprioceptors. Similarly the close connection with the cerebral cortex allows for a measure of control in the performance of movements and the integration of cortical movement impulses with the afferent information concerning the effect or effectiveness of these impulses.

At the cellular level this function of coordination and integration has been examined by Eccles (1967). In a simplified form the process of integration as outlined by Eccles may be described in the following way. There are only two types of afferent fibres which convey information to the cerebellum. These are the mossy fibres and the climbing fibres. Information from both sensory afferents and afferents from the cerebral cortex reach the cerebellar cortex via these types of fibre. The fibres differ both in their distribution and in their effects at the cerebellar cortical level. The climbing fibres link directly with single Purkinje cells in the cerebellar cortex and exert an excitatory influence upon them. The mossy fibres produce both inhibitory and excitatory influences upon the Purkinje cells. This is achieved by means of different mossy fibres taking alternative routes to the Purkinje cells. Those mossy fibres which exert an excitatory influence on the Purkinje cells pass directly to these cells in a way similar to the climbing fibres. Those which produce an inhibitory effect connect with cells known as Basket cells first of all. When stimulated the Basket cells produce inhibitory effects on the Purkinje cells with which they are connected. Since there are relatively few association fibres spreading from the Purkinje cells, the influence of any specific mossy fibre or climbing fibre is limited to a few square millimeters of cerebellar cortex. Somatotopic representation in the cerebellar cortex is possible because of this spatial restriction of cerebellar input.

Eccles argued that this arrangement of overlapping areas of inhibition and excitation provides the basis for integration of information. The integration occurs, however, in relatively autonomous units limited to areas affected by a particular fibre. Any particular signal may achieve representation as a component in many integration units. Thus '... the integration in the cerebellar cortex of afferent information occurs in multitudes (probably thousands) of subsets of the most diverse composition ...' (Eccles 1967, pp. 338). In this way a coordinating process can be achieved involving information from both higher (cerebral) and lower (sensory) centres. Since the integration of afferent information occurs in a 'piecemeal' fashion it is necessary to postulate that after the processing at a cerebellar level there is a further integrating mechanism elsewhere within the feedback loops. In this way coordination of all the subsets of integrated information from the cerebellar cortex occurs. In order to examine these areas of secondary integration it is necessary to consider the feedback loops in greater detail.

The efferent discharge from the cerebellum is solely by means of axons from the Purkinje cells which terminate either in the cerebellar nuclei or in the lateral vestibular nucleus. From these points fibres project either to the motor cortex or via the red nucleus into the descending sections of the spinal cord. Since the reciprocal relationship between the cerebellum and cerebral cortex has already been mentioned, it is clear that there are three interdependent feedback loops. Firstly, there is that loop which, beginning with the sensory receptors, proceeds to the cerebellum and thence to the motor cortex. Action in the motor cortex will therefore affect the ongoing movement causing a change in receptor activity and thus completing the feedback loop. A second feedback loop provides information from the integration centres within the cerebellum to the motor cortex. Efferents from the motor cortex pass not only down to the muscles involved in the movement but also, by way of the pontine nuclei and principal inferior olive, back to the cerebellar cortex. Finally, there is a feedback circuit operating between the cerebellum and the receptor systems. The cerebellum receives information from the peripheral receptors and after preliminary integration the impulses are directed via the red nucleus back into the rubrospinal tract of the spinal cord, thereby causing changes to occur in the evolving movement.

On the basis of these three feedback loops it is possible to speculate on the centres for secondary integration of impulses. Primary integration occurs at the level of the cerebellum. In the two feedback loops involving the cerebral cortex it is likely that there is further and more complete integration in the motor cortex before the transmission of new impulses to the muscles producing movement. The secondary integration for the final feedback loop between the cerebellum and the receptor systems is less easily determined. Eccles maintained that this is achieved by integration actually occurring within the spinal cord and in 'the evolving movement itself'. Although Eccles claimed that this concept was novel, a similar point was made by Paillard (1960). Paillard noted that what he called the 'spinal keyboard' does not receive commands and transmit them unaltered to the muscles. Rather, 'It already constitutes in itself an 'integrative' structure . . . This structure interprets the orders that it receives and transmits them only as a function of an ever changing state of receptivity' (Paillard, 1960, pp. 1686). Details of the feedback loops are given in diagrammatic form in Figure 5.

While analogies with servomechanisms do provide a lucid and useful way of describing and accounting for aspects of the control of motor behaviour,

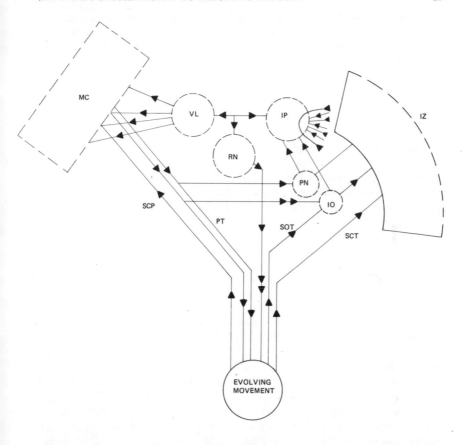

Fig. 5. Diagram of the complex pathways involved in the operational linkages of the intermediate zone, IZ, of the cerebellar cortex both to the motor cortex, MC, and to the spinal cord and so to the evolving movement. RN, red nucleus; IP, nucleus interpositus; IO, inferior olive; VL, ventro-lateral nucleus of the thalamus; PN, pontine nuclei, PT, pyramidal tract; SCP, spinocortical pathways; SOT, spinoolivary tract; SCT, spinocerebellar tract. (Eccles 1967).

they do not provide a complete explanation. Howard and Templeton (1966) point out that feedback mechanisms are inherently unstable. Any system which operates through error control is likely to reveal oscillatory tendencies and allow overshooting to take place. This instability is simply a direct function of, and proportional to, the transmission time for impulses to complete the circuit. It is evident from the above discussion that were these feedback systems the only means by which control occurred, then movement would not be smooth or accurate and there would be a tendency to overshoot targets. One function of the cerebellum may therefore be as a feedback stabilizing mechanism (see Ruch, 1951, 1965). Tendency to oscillate or overshoot may be further prevented by means of the cerebello-cerebral feedback loop. Ruch (1965) suggested that the motor cortex is incapable of planning movements in time, since impulses cannot be stored and discharged after some delay. However, if impulses from the motor cortex were discharged into the feedback loop involving the cerebellum, Ruch argued that a programming in time might be possible. 'The cerebellum might provide an accelerating or facilitating mechanism to impart velocity without over-shoot . . . A programming circuit with the correct delay characteristics would be helpful in decelerating movement to prevent overshoot or jerky stop. Movements so roughed in could be further refined by afferent sensory reports, either via the cerebellum or to the cerebral cortex by way of the spinothalamocortical fibres' (Ruch 1965, pp. 300).

On the basis of experimental evidence Gibbs (1954) postulated an alternative method by which overshooting of movements may be prevented. His suggestion was based on the possibility of rate control of movement. The extent of movement may be estimated, Gibbs maintained, by the integration of a known rate of movement over a known period of time. In order for this type of control to be possible it is necessary that even during continuous movement there are intermittent estimates of the position reached during movement. Gibbs concluded that, 'The principle of rate control clearly disposes of the main objections to feedback theory, i.e. that the known transmission latencies of the central nervous system preclude the possibility of current sensory control. The duration of movement (i.e. the integration period) is predetermined to allow for these latencies, and the continuity and rate correlation of the feedback impulses permits purposive control and modulation of the rates of movement before the limb has reached its final and intended position. This suggestion offers a viable alternative in the solution of the problem of overshooting.' (Gibbs 1954, pp. 37). The physiological basis of this form of integration has not been elucidated, but doubtless within the integration frameworks noted previously there is the possibility of this type of function.

The Reticular Formation of the Brainstem

The reticular formation of the brainstem is a phylogenetically old part of the central nervous system. It extends from the lower border of the medulla to the diencephalon. The formation consists of a mass of cells and short connecting fibres. These cellular masses appear to be largely undifferentiated, but recent evidence suggests that within the reticular formation there may be functionally independent nuclei (see French 1960, for a summary of modern findings).

The reticular formation merits attention because of its role within feedback mechanisms involving proprioception. The anatomical position and structure of the formation make it uniquely suitable for performing additional integrative functions of sensory and motor impulses.

Collaterals from all sensory afferents feed into the reticular formation from all sensory sources. It is therefore in a position to integrate information from different sensory sources. By means of a tonic inhibition mechanism, the formation is capable of decreasing the apparent sensitivity of sensory mechanisms. Decreases in this inhibitory function result in an apparent facilitating effect. In terms of proprioceptive information which is transmitted to the cortex, the role of the reticular formation is critical for perception to result from these impulses. Facilitation may cause increased sensitivity to this information and inhibition render perception less probable. There is also a reciprocal connection between the reticular formation and the cortex. The ascending reticular activating system produces a generalized arousing effect upon the cortex and the cortex is capable of stimulating the reticular formation. In this way cortical control over level of arousal or over the facilitation of particular sensory inputs may be the physiological basis of selective attention (Grossman 1967, provided a summary of these functions).

Increasingly the function of specific areas of the formation are being delimited. It is known with certainty that participation of the reticular formation is not restricted to feedback circuits involving the cortex. Granit and Kaada (1952) noted that there is a direct influence of the formation upon the gamma efferent feedback loop, mentioned above. Reticular activity appears to adjust the tension of the intrafusal muscle fibres through stimulation of the gamma system. Since the changes which occur in the intrafusal fibres have little or no effect upon the tension within the total muscle, the result is a bias in the spindles' afferent activity. Since it has also been established (Moruzzi, 1950) that the cerebellum has an inhibitory or facilitating influence upon the reticular formation, it is evident that the formation exerts an influence upon the proprioceptive feedback loops which do not have direct connection with the cortex.

Apart from a 'motor' influence through the gamma efferent system, the formation is also involved in modifying spinal reflexes. Whilst this role may be of relatively minor importance in man, of much greater significance may be the influence upon postural movements. There may be also modulation of specific motor commands from cortical or related extrapyramidal centres. These descending influences are thought to be both facilitory and inhibitory (Sprague and Chambers, 1954). Thus, the reticular formation serves as a modifying system in both afferent and efferent sides of the proprioceptive feedback circuits. Its total impact on these circuits cannot be stressed too highly. Since the formation has a similar influence on all sensory systems, its integrative functions in intersensory terms may be paralleled in importance only by the cerebellum and cortex.

Conclusion

There is now growing evidence that the most fruitful way of conceptualizing the physiological function of proprioception is as a series of interlocking feedback systems. The problem of providing details of the way in which these feedback systems operate is still a source of speculation and research. The relative importance of the various sub-systems within proprioception is not known with any degree of accuracy. There is also an absence of evidence concerning the relationship between the conscious and unconscious systems, their effect upon each other and the parameters of perception of movement at a physiological level. There is probably even greater ignorance concerning the physiological bases of interaction of proprioceptive and exteroceptive information. Although integrative centres such as the cerebellum have been identified, their mode of operation has not been analysed.

Ruch (1951), in his extensive discussion of the similarities between motor systems and servomechanisms, noted with some pessimism that, '. . . one may question the value of likening neural systems to servo systems. Such analogies, devoid of mathematical treatment, are essentially allegorical . . . Whether a mathematical treatment will lead to predictions capable of experimental verification remains to be seen. Otherwise we have added little since 1826 to Bell's "circle of nerves", (Ruch 1951 pp. 205-206). Although the development of mathematical treatments of feedback systems has become possible to some extent in other modalities, the proprioceptive feedback systems have not been analysed in this way during the two decades since Ruch's discussion. Consideration will be given to the problems causing these difficulties in later chapters.

3

THE
MEASUREMENT
OF
PROPRIOCEPTIVE
SENSITIVITY

Plate 1
    Weights used for establishing difference thresholds to proprioceptive cues.
(Courtesy of Lafayette Instrument Company).

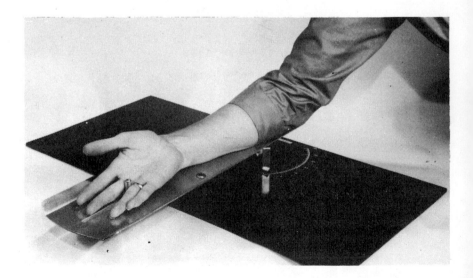

Plate 2
    A 'Kinesthesiometer' or instrument for measuring proprioceptive sensitivity in arm positioning. (Courtesy of Lafayette Instrument Company).

Chapter

3 THE MEASUREMENT OF PROPRIOCEPTIVE SENSITIVITY

Introduction

The disciplines which contribute to the understanding of movement have evolved distinct methods of measuring those aspects of movement relevant to their orientation. The problem of measuring proprioceptive sensitivity, therefore, has also been treated differently by contributing disciplines. The purpose of this chapter is to review some of the major methods of measuring this sensitivity and to examine the advantages and disadvantages of the techniques.

In brief, the following generalizations may be made. Physiologists have sought to establish the degree of physical stimulation necessary to produce responses in proprioceptive receptors. Investigations of this nature have obviously required the surgical treatment of the organism. While thresholds of stimulation in proprioceptors have been established using these methods for many species, the application of the techniques in man has not proved possible. Where the results of experiments have enabled generalizations to be made, the conclusions have been considered to apply to man as well as infrahuman organisms. Many of the results of such studies have already been presented in Chapter Two.

Psychologists have tended to concern themselves to a greater extent with proprioceptive sensitivity in man. The approach in this case has had two major objectives. Firstly, there have been attempts to establish man's capacity to detect body movement and changes in body movement. Secondly, there has been an increasing tendency to examine individual differences in sensitivity and to investigate the relevance of these differences to the performance of specific motor tasks. Although these principal objectives appear straightforward, their achievement has resulted in highly complex forms of measurement. Psychophysics, developing mainly in Germany during the nineteenth century, has emerged as a science of considerable intricacy. Major psychophysical techniques are discussed later in this chapter. The application of psychophysical techniques has generally employed small scale

35

movements. Physical educators have been more interested in estimating the accuracy of large movements, particularly those movements which form subcomponents of sports' skills. For many of these larger scale activities psychophysical techniques have proved unsuitable and alternative methods have been devised. The objectives of the physical educator and psychologist have been similar however. The physical educator has also been concerned with producing evidence of mean sensitivity to movement and examining the degree to which individual differences predict performance in motor skills. In some cases physical educators have investigated means for improving sensitivity in order that subjects may improve in the performance of a skill.

This distinction between the study of gross and fine movement in physical education and psychology is disappearing to some extent. It is apparent from reviews of recent literature that physical educators are increasingly exploiting the advantages of control which can be derived in the use of small scale movements and employing psychophysical techniques.

Perhaps one persistent difference between these disciplines has been the tendency for physical educators to be involved in the study of active movement, whereas at least a proportion of studies in psychology have involved the measurement of proprioceptive sensitivity to passively experienced movement. Although it is customary to distinguish between these two forms of movement, the distinction may not be quite so clear-cut as it seems. Lloyd and Caldwell (1965) measured accuracy of both active and passive movement. They also examined electromyographic records of these movements. Their conclusion was that ostensibly passive movement is not necessarily entirely without muscular activity. Movement produced by an experimenter in a passive organism may still result in that organism actively participating in some way. The qualitative distinction therefore between passivity and activity may in fact be a quantitative distinction after all.

All contributors to the study of proprioceptive sensitivity tend to restrict their measures to simple elements of total sensitivity. Some early attempts were made at establishing a score of 'total' proprioceptive sensitivity. The reason for the failures of these endeavours are discussed later.

The Validity and Reliability of Proprioceptive Measures

Physiological techniques of measuring the sensitivity of proprioceptors to stimulation have a distinct advantage over other techniques to be discussed. Having isolated a proprioceptor and caused it to be stimulated, a physiologist may feel assured that when some response occurs, he has established effectively and within his own terms of reference the sensitivity of that particular receptor. He may feel confident that his measure is valid. The psychologist and physical educator are not in such a fortunate position.

Dealing with intact human beings in which sensitivity can be measured only through indirect means, involves demonstrating adequately that what is measured is truly proprioceptive sensitivity and not some other attribute of the subject. Perhaps examples would serve to clarify this issue. In the classical technique of psychophysical study much of the research was carried out using sensitivity to lifted weights. Similarly, many modern tests have involved measurements of limb and body positioning. These tests, when conducted in the absence of visual cues, may appear to be valid measures of proprioceptive sensitivity. However, information may be available to the subject from cutaneous sensory sources providing additional cues concerning position, movement and weight. It has already been shown that different proprioceptors contribute at different times in the duration of movement (Chapter Two). Therefore, if a test involves limb positioning, parts of the movement may involve a greater contribution from one set of receptors than another. In other parts of the movement the relative importance of these sets of receptors may change. Even where the experimenter may be sure that no other sensory sources are contributing information therefore, it is still very difficult to decide exactly what aspects of proprioception are being measured.

There is greater sensitivity to movement when the responses involved are familiar to the subject than in those movements which are unfamiliar (Lloyd & Caldwell, 1965). This creates another, albeit minor, problem in the validity of proprioceptive measures. It is possible that what is being measured in tests involving movement is not sensitivity alone, but in part, the previous experience of the subject. Since there are likely to be individual differences in movement experience a test may reflect these differences in the score derived.

Another difficulty has arisen in the use of some active movement tests of proprioception. Proprioception includes the capacity to recognize limb positions. An instruction to a subject to move his arm to a position at 90 degrees to his body would appear, superficially, to test this capacity adequately. But, the assumption is made that all subjects equally comprehend the meaning of a 90 degree angle. This may not be a tenable assumption particularly when dealing with younger age groups. Similarly, as Smith (1969) pointed out, a test of this kind requires not only proprioceptive sensitivity, but also an adequate 'model of action'. The subject must comprehend the meaning of 90 degrees and must also have experience of moving to that position and have adequately remembered the movement. A test of this sort, therefore, may measure three different attributes which need not necessarily be highly correlated. Firstly, it could measure proprioceptive sensitivity *per se,* secondly, comprehension of the meaning of 90 degrees and, thirdly, 'proprioceptive memory'. Gibbs and Logan (1965) expressed a similar criticism.

Proprioception is manifest in a large proportion of movements of the intact organism. Any particular aspect of proprioception may often be measured in many different ways. The fact that so many alternatives exist has two salient disadvantages. Firstly, it makes the comparison of data derived from different studies difficult. Perhaps more relevant to this discussion is the fact that the number of alternatives also demands that assessments of degrees of validity be made by an investigator choosing a test. If proprioception is to be measured in the intact organism it is possible that some confounding attributes are always measured as well. These confounding attributes may vary both qualitatively and quantitatively from test to test. The selection of any particular test requires great care. For example, later in this chapter tests of balance and the proprioceptive sensitivity of the vestibular mechanisms are discussed. A test of vestibular function which requires the subject to balance on a beam may be confounded by other proprioceptive activity and the previous experience of the subject. Rotating the passive subject and observing the amount of acceleration detected by the subject may constitute another measure of vestibular function, but in this case the results may be confounded by cutaneous pressure cues. The question of which test is the more valid indicator of proprioceptive sensitivity of the inner ear mechanisms is one which is almost impossible to answer.

One problem which has seldom been discussed in relation to measures of proprioception concerns the relationship of proprioception to other sensory modalities. In the intact organism engaged in real-life activity, proprioceptive information is used in conjunction with other sensory information. In order to measure proprioceptive sensitivity however, it is normal to remove as many extraneous cues as possible. This act of isloation may in fact change the perception of proprioceptive information. If measures of proprioception have as their objective the assessment of proprioceptive sensitivity in the context of normal activity the procedure of isolating proprioceptors for measurement may not provide valid results. This argument may be applied at many different levels. The physiologist may be satisfied that a certain level of physical stimulation is necessary to cause firing in a single proprioceptor, but yet have no assurance that modification of that impulse will not occur at higher levels. In the same way, a psychologist may establish sensitivity to movement around a particular joint with a blindfolded subject, but cannot be certain that this is a reflection of movement sensitivity for that subject when the eyes are open. Simple changes in attentional factors may cause dramatic changes in perception under these two conditions.

Many of these problems of validation have not been solved. Most often the problem has been ignored. One solution has been to define proprioception in terms of the test used. For example, Fleischman and Rich (1963), in a study involving the relationship between proprioceptive sensitivity and motor learning, implicitly consider proprioceptive sensitivity to mean proprioceptive sensitivity *as measured by* capacity to discriminate between lifted weights. In this way the problem of validity is solved by the simple means of defining the attribute in terms of the test. Although one may criticize this method as avoiding the issue, it has great merits at a purely experimental level; the operational definition having become an established part of psychological experimentation.

A second technique, and one most common in tests purporting to measure the totality of proprioceptive sensitivity, has been to correlate scores on an individual test item with the achievement on the whole test battery. That is, a battery of tests with 'face validity' may be chosen and the correlation of any sub-test with the total score be regarded as a measure of that sub-test's validity (for example, see Roloff, 1953). The obvious drawback with such techniques is that the measure of validity is only as dependable as the original choice of tests with face validity. The assumption is also made that proprioception is a phenomenon in which all components necessarily correlate highly. Later evidence has tended to suggest that this is not the case (see Scott, 1955).

Some alternative techniques have been used for validation. Kerr and Weinlund (1933) demonstrated that one particular test of proprioception successfully discriminated between athletes and non-athletes. Others (for example Wiebe 1954) have used similar approaches. In proving that those who manifestly possess high levels of proprioceptive sensitivity perform in a way superior to those who do not, a measure of validation is achieved. This technique of validation again may be criticized since it is obvious that many other attributes contribute to athletic prowess apart from proprioceptive sensitivity. Also, this system may not be applicable in all situations. Many measures of proprioception may sample aspects of proprioception not related to athletic prowess or to any specific skill. In any case, the phrase 'manifestly possess high levels of proprioceptive sensitivity' begs many questions. However, where it is applicable this use of an external criterion has much to recommend it.

An attempt has been made by some authors, for example Scott (1955), to use a previous test of proprioception as an indicator of validity for their own. This technique, usually known as convergent validity, is of course only as good as the preceding test. It has the advantage, however, of providing a simple correlational measure of validity against some objective criterion.

The question of validity in proprioceptive measures is therefore one which has not been fully answered. Criticisms of specific tests apart from these general comments are made in this chapter.

Reliability

Tests of the reliability of proprioceptive measures have produced extremely divergent results. Although there are exceptions, greater reliability has been found in those measures involving fine movements rather than gross bodily movements. Many of the test batteries purporting to measure total proprioception were forced to reject test items because of unreliability. Smith (1969) argued that this unreliability stemmed from the fact that the tests were essentially invalid. Smith pointed out that many tests relied upon proprioceptive memory as well as proprioceptive sensitivity. She did not explain why this necessarily leads to unreliability. If a subject has a faulty 'model of action' his error score may be large but not necessarily inconsistent. The reasons for the unreliability of tests involving perception of proprioceptive cues in gross motor activities has not been satisfactorily explained. It may be that the 'model for action' has a large variance. That is, that the quality of remembered movements suffers distortion or change from test to test. An alternative hypothesis may be made on the basis of physiological evidence presented in Chapter Two. The fact that incoming sensory information is both integrated and variably inhibited prior to reaching central processing areas suggests that it is possibly these physiological variables which create the unreliability of the tests. If it is the case that proprioceptive sensitivity is not a stable attribute but one in which fluctuations occur, this may also explain why measures of reliability involving split-half techniques or internal consistency measures have generally produced superior results.

Psychophysical Measurement

Psychophysics was the name given by Fechner in 1860 to the study of the relationship between mind and body. Although Fechner's philosophical objectives have lost much of their relevance today, his techniques of measurement formed the basis of the modern science of psychophysics. Many modern texts give extensive treatment to the problems and advantages of psychophysics and Engen (1971) and Stevens (1951) are particularly recommended. The aim of psychophysical study is to measure the relationship between sensation and stimulation by means of subjects' reports. In proprioceptive study, for example, a subject may be asked whether a particular passively experienced arm movement is greater or smaller than a standard arm movement. Alternatively, he may be asked whether he feels any arm movement at all. By taking repeated measures of the subject's accuracy in responding to some form of stimulation a general picture or mean sensitivity of the subject's accuracy in that context may be obtained. Obviously the testing procedure needs to be stringently controlled and several attempts have been made to establish psychophysical methods which allow the computation of a statistically sound estimate of the subject's sensitivity.

Because of the unfamiliarity of psychophysical procedures to most subjects, one problem which occurred in this form of testing was the improvement in performance of subjects over initial test trials. This is usually circumvented by allowing the subject to practise the activity of the test before any real measures are taken, thus improving the reliability and consistency of the measures. Even with practice, many subjects have been shown to produce response biases, that is, a tendency to produce one type of answer rather than another. Modern psychophysical techniques have gone some way towards solving this problem by providing statistical treatments which compensate for these response biases.

Stevens (1951) identified seven major categories of problems in psychophysics.

1 *Absolute thresholds*. What are the stimulus values that mark the transition between response and no response on the part of the organism?
2 *Differential threshold*. What is the resolving power of the organism; i.e. what is the smallest detectable change in a stimulus?
3 *Equality*. What values of two different stimuli produce the same response (i.e. appear equal on the scale of some attribute)?
4 *Order*. What different stimuli produce a set of responses or psychological impressions that can be set in serial order?
5 *Equality of intervals*. What stimuli produce a set of responses successively equidistant on the scale of some attribute?
6 *Equality of ratios*. What stimuli produce a set of responses bearing constant ratios to one another on the scale of some attribute?
7 *Stimulus rating*. With what accuracy (validity) and precision (reliability) can a person estimate the physical value of a stimulus?

The first two problems have received by far the greatest amount of attention within studies of proprioception. An absolute threshold may be simply described as the point along a continuum of stimulation which produces sensation. Engen (1971) used an appropriate example. If a blindfolded subject has a minute weight placed on his hand, so small that he cannot feel it, his response may be 'no, there is no weight present'. If that weight is gradually increased until the subject reports that weight can be felt then the borderline or threshold from no-sensation to sensation has been crossed. If the process is repeated on numerous occasions it is possible for an accurate assessment of that subject's absolute threshold to be made. An arbitrary decision is usually made that the point on the continuum of stimulation which is correctly detected on 50 per cent of the trials is designated the absolute threshold.

The measurement of absolute thresholds in proprioception has been concerned with the detection of passively experienced movement of the limbs and the whole body, the detection of body rotation, body tilt and acceleration. There are obvious limitations in the number of proprioceptive attributes for which absolute thresholds may be established. Active movement absolute thresholds may not be measured for example. It is not possible for an experimenter to require a subject to move the arm a fraction of an inch for example and then ask the subject if he experienced any sensation of movement.

In determining differential or difference thresholds the experimenter seeks to measure the accuracy with which a subject detects a difference between two stimuli both of which are greater than the absolute threshold. The subject's task therefore is a process of comparison rather than detection *per se*. In this case, a subject may be presented with a standard stimulus (for example, a weight of 100 grams) and be required to lift this weight using a standardised technique. A subsequent weight may be presented which weighs only 90 grams and the subject be required to report whether the second weight is heavier, equal to or lighter than the first weight or standard. As the weight of the comparison stimulus is increased, a point is reached at which the subject can no longer detect any difference. In this way a different kind of threshold is crossed; from 'difference detected' to 'no-difference detected'. Both upper and lower difference thresholds may be established, the former is regarded as the point where the subject changes his decision from 'equality' to 'heavier' in respect to the comparison weight. These two thresholds delimit a section of the continuum of stimulation in which the subject cannot detect differences between the standard and comparison weights. For this reason the distance in stimulation units between these two thresholds is known as the interval of uncertainty. The difference threshold is computed by dividing the magnitude of the interval of uncertainty by two. (Since the interval of uncertainty is a measure of two thresholds, both upper and lower). Difference thresholds in proprioception have been established for lifted weights, arm movements, and finger movements, and some vestibular functions.

Several alternative methods for determining these two kinds of thresholds have been developed. That which most closely approximates the brief descriptions given above is the Method of Limits. In this system the threshold is approached from both above and below on the continuum of stimulation. Ascending and descending series of comparison stimuli are presented, the comparison stimulus being changed by regular small amounts. An alternative to this technique is found in the Method of Adjustment. This is a similar method but one which is suitable only where it is feasible for the subject, rather than the experimenter, to manipulate the comparison stimulus. Although the Method of Limits may be used where the scale of stimulation is of either a continuous or non-continuous nature, it has generally been used with scales in which discrete steps of the stimulus are preferable. The Method of Adjustment, however, is generally used where the scale is continuous. In this method the subject is presented with a standard stimulus and required to manipulate a second stimulus until the two appear to him to be the same. The difference threshold in this case may be assessed by the variability of the subject around the correct value over a number of trials. Quite frequently the standard deviation is used to indicate the difference threshold. The difference threshold is not derived from the interval of uncertainty and this value is sometimes arbitrarily defined as the inter-quartile range of error when the Method of Adjustment is used. This technique can also be applied to obtain the absolute threshold. The subject regulates the stimulus to that value which he considers to be the lowest it is possible for him to detect. The absolute threshold is defined by the mean value of repeated trials.

A third method which is sometimes used is the Method of Constant Stimuli. This technique is very similar to the Method of Limits except that two categories of response are allowed the subject in determining the difference threshold. The subject must decide whether the stimulus is greater than or smaller than the standard and is not allowed to respond that they are equal. For this reason a slight adjustment is made in the method of scoring. Since the subject can make only two responses, there is a probability of 0.5 that the correct answer will be given by chance. The difference threshold therefore, is designated as that value above or below the standard which is judged correctly on 75 per cent of the trials. The absolute threshold is computed in the same way as in the Method of Limits.

The use of these systems with their modifications and refinements has enabled many generalizations to be made concerning the absolute and difference thresholds in all sensory modalities.

Absolute Thresholds in Proprioception

Absolute thresholds in proprioception have been determined with passively experienced movement. In one of the earliest and most comprehensive surveys (Goldscheider, 1889, reported in Boring, 1942) the absolute thresholds for passive movement were established using movement around nine different joints. On the basis of more than 4,000 observations, Goldscheider was able to make the following generalizations. Firstly, movement around the larger joints is more readily detected than movement· around the smaller ones. This may also be interpreted as meaning that the proximal joints are more sensitive than the distal joints. Goldscheider demonstrated that the hip joint is more sensitive than the ankle for example, and similarly that the shoulder joint is more sensitive than the wrist or finger joints. These results were obtained using a fixed rate of movement of 0.3° per second. With this rate it was found that in the poorest or least sensitive joints the degree of displacement necessary for detection was greater than 1 degree whereas the most sensitive required only 0.2 degrees of displacement for accurate detection.

Goldscheider's work has been replicated many times and extended by others to include other joints. The results of later studies have shown, as it would be expected, that the rate of movement used in testing has an influence on the absolute threshold for passive movement. However, the precise interaction between rate of movement and threshold for movement has not been established. Corso (1967) presented the results of five independent investigators of the absolute threshold for passive movement at the elbow joint. The range of movement speed was from 0.08° per second to 0.33° per second. The range of thresholds was found to be from 0.3 degrees to 0.8 degrees. The results did not vary systematically and so far as the author is aware this interaction has not been explained.

Goldscheider also noted that the sensitivity of a joint is independent of a joint's position. This finding led Howard and Templeton (1966) to suggest that this indicates relatively little contribution from the muscle receptors in the perception of joint position. This psychophysical evidence therefore supports the conclusion, (mentioned in Chapter Two) by Smith (1969) that the muscle receptors play little part in the conscious appreciation of movement. There is evidence from Lloyd and Caldwell (1965) which contradicts Goldscheider's finding. They found that in movement around the knee joint there is greater sensitivity within the arc of the leg employed in walking than at extremes of the range.

Cleghorn and Darcus (1952) examined both absolute movement thresholds and thresholds for the detection of direction of movement. They found that for the elbow joint there was greater sensitivity to movement than to its direction. That is, there appears to be a lower threshold for the detection of movement than for the detection of direction. Furthermore, and again perhaps in contradiction of Smith's (1969) contention, Cleghorn and Darcus established that there is greater sensitivity to both the occurrence of movement and to its direction during extension than during flexion.

In the determination of absolute thresholds in those proprioceptive studies mentioned above, data have been derived using subjective reports. In the measurement of absolute thresholds for vestibular activity two different methods are also available. Use has been made of the oculogyral effect, for example. This effect is described as the apparent movement of a point of light when the subject is otherwise in the dark. Following stimulation of the vestibular system the oculogyral effect is likely to occur and may be used as an indicator of vestibular threshold. Secondly, observation of nystagmus in the subject may give a similar indication of vestibular function. Nystagmus is the rhythmic movement of the eyes brought about by the stimulation of the vestibular system. The choice of measuring technique for establishing absolute thresholds for vestibular functions has depended upon practical considerations and upon the aspect of vestibular functioning to be tested. For example, nystagmus may be used for testing only rotary thresholds.

Because of the diverse testing techniques, there are wide discrepancies in the determination of absolute threshold for rotary acceleration. The variations are from 2.0 degrees/second^2 (Dodge, 1923) to 0.12 degrees/second^2 (Graybiel, Kerr and Bartley, 1948). Broadly speaking it appears that the oculogyral illusion is the most sensitive measure, nystagmus being slightly less sensitive and subjective reports producing the highest threshold.

The vestibular mechanisms also provide information concerning linear acceleration. There appear to be wide individual differences in absolute thresholds for this attribute and the threshold also appears to be dependent upon the direction of acceleration. For vertical acceleration, Armstrong (1943) found a range of from 4 to 12 centimetres/second^2. On the other hand in horizontal acceleration, Clark and Graybiel (1949) found a range of from 2 to 20 centimetres/second^2.

One interesting study by MacCorquodale (1948) used trained aviators as subjects in an attempt to measure absolute thresholds for the detection of bank in an aeroplane. It was found in this study that a 15 degree angle of bank was necessary for accurate detection. In other terms, this may be described as an acceleration force of 0.15 degrees/second^2. This study also required the experienced subjects to estimate the angle of bank when blindfolded. Large errors were found in all estimates. In a $10°$ bank the mean error was over $4°$ and in a $60°$ bank the mean error was almost $12°$.

In the absence of rotary acceleration what degree of body tilt can be detected? This is a related problem in the determination of absolute thresholds for vestibular function. Body tilt measures have generally been made with the subject strapped into a chair which may be tilted in several different planes. With the subjects blindfolded this method ostensibly indicates vestibular accuracy in the detection of deviation from the upright. However, it has not been found possible to discount the role of other sensory systems in detecting body tilt. It is very difficult to prevent cutaneous and muscular cues.

Most of the studies are agreed upon reporting that mean absolute threshold for body tilt, by whatever means this is perceived, lies between $2°$ and $3°$. McFarland (1945) concurred with this estimate, but pointed out that there are wide individual differences. McFarland found that some subjects, for example, required as much as 14 degrees of tilt before accurate detection occurred.

In general the results of studies of absolute thresholds in proprioception have tended to reveal a high degree of accuracy in man. Smith (1969) cautioned that there is a danger in regarding absolute thresholds as true indicators of sensitivity in real life movement situations. In the first place, movement velocities have generally speaking been very low in the testing situation compared with movement velocities found in real life activity. Secondly, absolute thresholds have been determined using passively experienced movement. Sensitivity in active movement which constitutes a majority of real-life movement need not necessarily correlate highly with sensitivity in passive situations.

Difference Thresholds in Proprioception

In all modalities difference thresholds have been examined in order to establish whether there exist common properties of the difference threshold. Investigation was most intense during the nineteenth century and culminated in the Weber-Fechner Law. Since the nineteenth century this law has been refined and exceptions to the law discovered but the law still forms a major facet of psychophysical knowledge (see Stevens 1951). Put in its simplest form, the law suggests that as the physical or objective value of a stimulus increases logarithmically the subjective sensation by an observer is one of arithmetic increase. One of the obvious consequences of this law is the effect on the difference threshold. Using an example from proprioception may clarify this. If an increase of 10 grams is necessary for detection of a difference in lifting a 100 gram weight, the Weber-Fechner law predicts that if the standard weight is changed to 1,000 grams a 100 gram addition is necessary for a difference to be detected. Small changes are easily detected when the stimulus value is close to the absolute threshold, but very large changes may be necessary for detection when the stimulus value is high. Weber concluded in mathematical terms that:

$$\Delta I = KI,$$

where ΔI is the increment to a stimulus necessary for detection (a just noticeable difference, or j.n.d.)

I is the stimulus value
and K is a constant.

The formula may also be written, of course:

$$\Delta I/I = K, \text{ known as the Weber fraction.}$$

That is, the necessary increment divided by the stimulus intensity is a constant.

Although this law has been criticized, especially in terms of its capacity to predict difference thresholds when the absolute threshold is approached and at high levels of stimulus intensity, slight modifications to the basic fraction have kept the law in use in psychophysics. As Granit (1955) said, 'Nevertheless, despite the validity of much of the criticism directed against it, . . . (the Weber-Fechner Law) . . . has survived every attack. The psychophysicists of today still keep it in their arsenal as a convenient rule of thumb to be taken down from the shelf whenever difference thresholds are discussed'. (Granit, 1955, p. 11). Some of the more important criticisms are discussed in the next section.

In Chapter Two the enormous impact of Adrian and Matthews' work on physiological research was described. The capacity for recording from single sense organs enabled the physiological investigation of many sensory inputs in unprecedented detail. This development also made possible the physiological investigation of the Weber-Fechner Law. Adrian (1926) showed that nerve impulses reflected the intensity of a stimulus by variations in frequency of discharge. Matthews (1931), examining proprioception in the frog, demonstrated that impulse frequency is proportional to the logarithm of the stimulus. This would be predicted on the basis of the Weber-Fechner Law. The law proposed during the nineteenth century concerning sensation, therefore, was shown to reflect fundamental physiological activity.

By far the greatest amount of research in psychological studies into proprioceptive difference thresholds has involved lifted weights. The concensus has been that the (K) constant in the formula for lifted weights is of the order of 1/30. That is, a one gram difference in 30 is likely to be detected or a 2 gram difference in 60, etc. Corso (1967) reported that in a study by Oberlin (1936) in which five different standards were used, variations occurred in the difference thresholds. The mean interval of uncertainty (2 x the difference threshold) was 3gms where the standard weight was 25gms and 45gms when the standard used was 600gms. There are also individual differences in the capacity to judge lifted weights. Dickinson (1969), using a sample size of N = 33 found difference thresholds of from 2 to 10 grams using a standard weight of 100 grams.

Henry (1953) examined difference thresholds in response to pressure change. The subject was required to push against a handhold, behind which a spring attached to an irregular cam varied the force. Subjects reported any changes in pressure of which they became aware. Henry found that sensitivity varied systematically with rate of pressure change. The results were expressed as a Weber ratio (or the percentage change in the stimulus required for a discrimination of the change). The range was from 4.9 per cent for the most rapid pressure changes to 8.9 per cent for the slowest of pressure changes. One interesting aspect of this study was the comparison of these data with measures of the subjects' ability to maintain constant pressure on the handle. Mean error in response was a force of 0.71 lbs. When the data for subjective reports of changes were expressed in these terms a perception of mean value 1.25 lbs was found. The implication is that man may be capable of responding to pressure cues which are not perceived at a conscious level. It should be noted that Henry's results are likely to reflect sensitivity to both cutaneous and proprioceptive sources.

Martenuik, Shields and Campbell (1972) conducted a study in an attempt to measure difference thresholds and absolute errors in the reproduction of amplitudes of standard horizontal arm movements. Using three arm movements of 45 degrees, 90 degrees and 125 degrees difference thresholds of 1.95 degrees, 2.20 degrees and 2.13 degrees were reported. These difference thresholds were not significantly different from each other. As Martenuik et al pointed out, these data reveal high levels of response sensitivity. When the results were examined in terms of constant errors it was shown that small movements were constantly over-estimated and large movements under-estimated.

In recent years there has been a reduction in the amount of psychophysical research into proprioception using the classical methods. One of the reasons for this has been the accumulation of evidence suggesting that many factors may influence thresholds derived by psychophysical means. For example, Corso (1967) maintained that changes in weight sensitivity could be produced by alterations in the method by which the weights were lifted. He noted increasing sensitivity from wrist only used in lifting to elbow movement allowed, and with greatest sensitivity if shoulder movement was also permitted. This provides additional support for Goldscheider's (1889) contention that the proximal joints are more sensitive than the distal joints. In this case, however, it was weight sensitivity rather than movement which was measured.

Robinson (1969) also demonstrated that learning occurred in a weight discrimination task and improvement was found in mean performance of subjects over a number of trials.

Sekuler (1965) found that the capacity to discriminate weights is partially dependent upon duration of exposure to the stimulus. It was found that sensitivity increased over the range of 100 to 400 m. seconds.

Ross and Gregory (1964) reported that difference thresholds for lifted weights may also be subject to a size-weight illusion. They found that the magnitude of the difference threshold was dependent upon the size of the weight. Using two sets of stimuli which were identical in weight but different in size there were significant differences in the thresholds derived. The difference threshold for a small set of weights was greater than for a large set. Subjects therefore may not judge weights only in terms of proprioceptive and cutaneous information derived from lifting, but also be influenced by other factors.

Proprioception and Stevens' Power Law

Many of the above criticisms of traditional psychophysical methods are practical in nature. That is, they concern difficulties in the procedures of measurement. Much more serious criticism has come from Stevens (1961). Stevens made the claim that psychophysics had been '. . . sidetracked for a hundred years, mainly by Fechner's diligence in behalf of his famous logarithmic law'. Instead of a logarithmic law, Stevens proposed a power law. The distinction between the power law and the Weber-Fechner law may be summed up in the following way. The Weber-Fechner proposition was essentially that equal stimulus *ratios* correspond to equal sensation *differences*. Stevens' power law on the other hand claims that equal stimulus *ratios* correspond to equal sensation *ratios*.

In order to test this proposition, new techniques of measurement had to be developed. These measures involved asking subjects to estimate the subjective magnitudes of stimuli. This procedure of magnitude estimation has since been used successfully in many different modalities. For example, a subject may be required to listen to a number of tones varying in loudness. The subject assigns any number which he considers appropriate to the first sound and in subsequent presentations tries to assign a number proportional to the new sounds. Other numerical procedures have been produced with varying success in meeting the problem of supplying direct measures of sensation.

The result of these procedures was Stevens' power law. The law states in mathematical terms, that the subjective magnitude of a sensation is proportional to the objective magnitude of the stimulus raised to a power n. Or:—

$$\psi = K\phi n$$

where ψ = subjective magnitude of stimulus (what Stevens called the psychological magnitude), and K = a constant determined by the units of measurement. The value of n is dependent upon the attribute measured. ϕ is the physical or objective value of the stimulus. A modification may be made to this part of the equation which takes into account the fact that the measurement of the effective physical stimulus must start from the particular threshold of the stimulus in the conditions of the experiment. The equation may be written as:—

$$\psi = K(\phi - \phi_0)^n$$

where ϕ_0 is the threshold for that stimulus under the experimental conditions obtaining.

Increasingly the power law has been found to describe psychophysical data more accurately than the Weber-Fechner law. The power law has not gone uncriticized however. Much of the criticism has revolved around the use of subjective numerical reports being used as measurements. This criticism has been met (see Stevens 1962) by means of cross-modality validations. That is, rather than having subjects assign numbers they have been asked to squeeze a hand-dynamometer for example. The results from the cross-modality studies support the data derived verbally with only insignificant discrepancies.

Although it may appear from the foregoing discussion that the power law and the Weber-Fechner law cannot both be right, an attempt has been made by Ekman (1964) to reconcile the two points of view. Ekman suggested that if the assumption is made that Fechner's law is correct and if it is assumed that a subject reacts to *number* stimulation according to Fechner's law, then it is possible to derive the power law from Fechner's law. Or, as Ekman (1964) suggested, 'In this sense the derivation of the power function is based on a generalization of Fechner's law. According to the model, a direct scaling method is a procedure in which the subject *matches* two sets of stimuli'.

Stevens and his co-workers have assessed the value of the exponent n for three aspects of proprioception. Lifted weights showed an exponent of 1.45 (Stevens and Galanter 1957) and the force of handgrip as measured by a hand dynamometer, an exponent of 1.70 (Stevens and Mack 1959). It should be noted that a linear relationship would mean an exponent of 1.00. That is, an exponent greater than 1.00 indicates that the psychological value of a stimulus grows more quickly than the physical value. Most of the stimulus continua which have been measured in proprioception have given exponents larger than 1.00. Stevens and Stone (1959) found that subjective thickness as measured by finger span grows as a power function of stimulus width, with an exponent of 1.33.

Stevens' work has stimulated a number of other investigations into the relevance of the power law to proprioceptive sensitivity. Ronco (1963) investigated the extent of arm movement and discovered a power function of 1.08. More recently Hoff (1971) examined five different aspects of proprioceptive sensitivity: thickness, as measured by finger span, extent of arm movement, heaviness of lifted weights, force by handgrip and speed of arm movement. Most of these tests were effectively replications of previous experiments, although different apparatus and procedures were used in some cases. Only the test of speed of movement was unique to this experiment. Hoff found the following exponents:— thickness = 0.97, extent of movement = 1.21, weight = 1.43, speed of movement = 1.54, and force = 1.56. All these estimates differ to a greater or lesser extent from previous studies. However, Hoff considered that her results differ only as a product of the different experimental procedures and situations. Perhaps the most significant of these results is the very close approach to linearity (0.97) found in thickness judgements, especially since this exponent is the only one which falls below the level of linearity, 1.00. According to Hoff '. . . psychological thickness' does not grow quite as rapidly as stimulus thickness.

It is possible to regard the deviation of an exponent from 1.00 as a reflection of that sense's accuracy. In other words, if sensory events reflect physical stimuli exactly, a 1.00 exponent would be derived. From the results of Hoff's work the order in which the results are listed above also depicts the order of accuracy for those aspects of proprioception. Since Hoff used the same subjects for all five tests this is a more legitimate comparison than that usually possible across studies.

Martenuik and Ryan (1972) examined angular arm movements using Stevens' methods. Ten physical distances were used varying in size from 20 to 100 degrees and presented in random order. The subject was asked to move his straight arm horizontally toward the mid-line of the body from a constant starting point until it reached a wooden stopper. This acted as a standard movement. Using the ratio scaling method of fractionation developed by Stevens, Martenuik and Ryan found that the power function best described their data. In this case the exponent was 1.075. This exponent is somewhat closer to 1.00 than Hoff (1971) found for extent of non-angular movement, but Martenuik and Ryan noted that Hoff's (1.21), Ronco's (1.08) and their own (1.075) exponents '. . . are within the limits quoted by Stevens (1961) as acceptable differences among exponents of comparable power functions'.

Proprioception and Theory of Signal Detection

In part the reduction in the use of classical psychophysical methods has also been due to the advent of the theory of signal detection (TSD). This theory had its origins in the mid-1950s (Tanner and Swets, 1954; Munson and Karlin, 1956) and resulted from the combination of two previous theories. As Green (1960) noted, TSD had as its parents statistical decision theory and the theory of ideal observers. The major distinction between the traditional psychophysical method and the theory of signal detection is that in TSD the concept of the threshold is abandoned. Instead, as Swets (1961) has suggested; 'The theory of ideal observers makes it possible to relate the level of the detection performance attained by a real observer to the mathematically ideal performance. The mathematical ideal is the upper limit on the detection performance that is imposed by the environment. This limit is stated in terms of measurable parameters of the signal and of the masking noise for a variety of signal and noise'.

Two assumptions are made concerning sensory responses to signals. Firstly, it is assumed that the sensory response is variable for a given physical stimulus. The sensory response is thought to fluctuate as a product of extraneous environmental factors, or because fluctuation is introduced purposefully by the experimenter, or is inherent in the sensory system. 'Noise' is assumed to be present always. Secondly, the sensory response is assumed to be a unidimensional variable. A subject, deciding on the presence or absence of a stimulus, is assumed to make a decision on the basis of his sensory response. Neither the noise nor the signal is constant in its effect and both may be thought of as frequency distributions around some mean value for noise alone and for signal plus noise. If these two distributions overlap it is not possible for the subject to be correct on all trials in detecting signals. It is assumed therefore that the subject adopts some criterion (see Fig. 6).

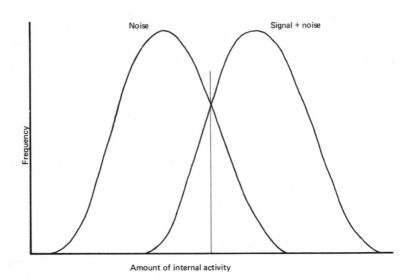

Fig. 6. Hypothetical curves of the distribution of varying amounts of internal activity for noise alone and signal + noise. The criterion line indicates the optimal position for this distribution if the subject wishes to minimize both missed signals and false positives. Amounts of internal activity above the criterion will be judged as 'signal present', and below the criterion as 'no signal present'.

Above this criterion point, the amount of sensory response experienced by the subject prompts him to give a positive response and below the criterion he responds with 'no signal present'. The criterion is thought to be flexible and its position depends on the instructions to the subject and the experimental situation.

The advantages of TSD over a psychophysical approach have been enumerated by Fitts and Posner (1967) as:

1. TSD allows for the computation of a sensory capacity; and
2   the effects of sensory capacity may be distinguished from those of instruction, motivation and competing signals.

In the classical psychophysical studies it is not possible to establish the stringency with which an observer makes his judgements and which affects the threshold. In TSD it is possible to determine whether the subject is using a low-certainty criterion (leading to a low threshold) or a high-certainty criterion with a correspondingly high threshold (Corso, 1967).

TSD has been applied experimentally to proprioceptive study to only a minimal degree. The reasons are probably two-fold. Firstly, the pioneers in TSD were involved in the areas of vision and audition. Inertia has probably sustained the interest in those fields. Secondly, and perhaps of greater importance, are the enormous number of problems associated with the experimental application of TSD to proprioception. The major problem concerns the quantification of signal to noise ratios. In proprioceptive terms, signals may be thought of as occurring against a background of proprioceptive activity. However, since this activity is internally produced and has its origins in the whole of the body, it is not possible for this noise level to be assessed quantitatively. That is, when stimulus and noise are not capable of exact manipulation by the experimenter, the quantitative aspect of TSD cannot be determined.

Although this experimental problem may not be simply resolved, it does not invalidate the use of the theoretical structure on a hypothetical basis. It is instructive, for example, to think of skilled behaviour in these terms. This is considered in greater detail later, but an outline may be given at this point. During the performance of a task the subject may be required to respond to various internally produced signals. These are likely to occur against a background of proprioceptive information. The capacity of a subject to detect those relevant stimuli or signals and respond to them, may in some measure delimit that subject's level of performance. From an alternative point of view, the capacity of a teacher to instruct a subject in the optimal placement of a criterion or to provide feedback concerning whether or not a relevant signal occurred, is likely to be a measure of the teacher's efficiency. Therefore, although quantification has not been achieved in the application of TSD to proprioception, the theory may have considerable merit as a means of viewing the role of proprioception in the acquisition of skill.

The terminology of TSD has also become a part of the vocabulary of proprioception in terms of measures of sensitivity even though the theory may not be applied in detail. Lloyd and Caldwell (1965) for example, in showing that in the extremes of movement around the knee joint a reduction in accuracy of detecting position occurs, noted that one hypothesis which may be advanced for this is that '. . . pressure on the (joint) capsule created by the increased flexion of the limb beyond the normal range of movement could be considered as a potential source of noise in the afferent channel produced by the distortion of the capsule'. The inference being that increased 'noise' leads to a decrease in signal detection.

Other Proprioceptive Measures involving Fine Movements

Apart from the measurement of difference and absolute thresholds there are further measures of proprioception which have involved small scale muscular activity. Howard and Templeton (1966) listed a set of 'kinaesthetic judgements' divided on the basis of active and passive participation of the subject. Their list includes:—

For passive movement—
1   thresholds of movement
2   position judgement and accuracy of directional judgments
3   accuracy of judgments of amplitude and speed of movement.

For active movement—
1   steadiness and fineness of movement
2   judgment of position
3   the accuracy of direction, amplitude, pressure and speed of movement.

Evidence has been presented already for some of these judgments. There is, however, a lack of evidence for many of the other types of judgment. Many of the studies for example which are quoted by Howard and Templeton have involved the use of vision as well as proprioceptive information, especially in the accuracy of fine active movements.

One of the first experiments in this field and one which examined accuracy both with the eyes open and closed came from Woodworth (1899). These studies also examined the effects on accuracy of distance and rate variations. The experiments involved the subjects producing pencil strokes to the beat of a metronome. It was shown that in the case in which the control of movement was most clearly the result of proprioception (with eyes closed) there was a slight improvement in accuracy with increasing rate for the dominant hand. When the non-dominant hand was tested, accuracy and rate were inversely correlated. In a further experiment accuracy was related to the distance moved when time per movement was held constant. It was found that with the eyes closed, there was an increase in the errors made. Perhaps this result is to be anticipated, but interestingly enough, the rate of increase of errors with eyes closed was smaller than the rate of increase in errors when the eyes were open.

Others have been concerned with the accuracy with which the limbs may be actively positioned in the absence of visual information. Many of the more successful of these studies have involved the measurement of error in the bilateral positioning of the limbs. Slinger and Horsley (1906) required subjects to place a finger of both hands at equal points on two sides of a glass sheet. The errors were measured in terms of the distance which separated the fingers. It was found that errors increased with the distance from the body and as angular displacement increased from the midline of the sagittal plane of the body. Recently Robinson (1969) produced a similar type of test which he found suitable and reliable for use with children. Blindfolded children were required to move two parallel blocks along grooves from opposite ends of a stand until they believed they were opposite to each other. Errors were judged in terms of the distance apart of the two blocks after each trial.

Lloyd and Caldwell (1965), in their study cited earlier in this chapter, examined the relationship between active and passive accuracy in leg positioning. The lower leg was used for the experiment and a splint was employed to immobilize the leg except at the knee joint. Lloyd and Caldwell moved the leg passively in one part of the experiment and required subjects to indicate the joint angle achieved after movement. In that part of the experiment employing active movement the subject was required to move his leg to specified joint angles. The results of the study indicated a greater accuracy of positioning when movement was active rather than passive. An exception to this was found at the extremes of the 100 degree range used by Lloyd and Caldwell, where passive movement was shown to be more accurate. Lloyd and Caldwell attributed this distinction partly to the familiarity of subjects with the proprioceptive information derived in the walking-arc of the lower leg.

Accuracy of active arm positioning was examined by Phillips and Summers (1954). Subjects were exposed to a particular arm movement and asked to replicate that movement. Phillips and Summers also arrived at the conclusion that familiarity of movement influenced the degree of sensitivity since they found smaller error scores with the dominant arm. Also they noted that error scores did not vary systematically with the degrees of arc moved. That is, it was not necessarily the larger movements which showed greater errors. The more accurate movements were those which Phillips and Summers considered were more typical of movements found in every day life.

Some contradictory evidence in the accuracy of arm positioning has come from Caldwell (1956) and Caldwell and Herbert (1956). They found that the accuracy of arm positioning was dependent upon the locus of the goal position and also upon the direction of the primary adjustive movement. In almost direct contradiction of Lloyd and Caldwell's (1965) work on the knee joint and of the work by Phillips and Summers (1954), positioning accuracy tended to increase as the extremes of arm flexion and extension were approached and to decrease in more medial positions. They suggested that the relaxation associated with movement from positions of extreme flexion or extension results in poorer performance in the detection of position.

Gibbs and Logan (1965) reported a series of experiments involving the use of proprioceptive cues in directing the positioning of the head and eyes. Subjects had their arms hidden from view and passively moved to one of several positions. The head or eyes were then moved actively until the subject considered head or eyes were pointing in the same direction as the arm. These investigators found very high levels of accuracy in this form of positioning. In one study the mean error was only 0.28 degrees. They claimed that this high level of accuracy possibly underestimated subject capacity.

Measures of Body Balance

One of the significant aspects of proprioceptive measurement using gross body movement has come in the form of measures of body balance of various kinds. Balancing is essentially an activity requiring intersensory co-operation, but those studies which have examined body balance in the absence of visual cues are perhaps most significant in this context. The fact that vision does play an important part in ability to balance has been effectively demonstrated by both Dickinson (1968a) and Leonard (1966). Leonard for example demonstrated that blind children have great difficulty in standing on a balance beam, and, as one would expect, showed balance ability scores inferior to sighted children. These blind children were also found to balance no better than sighted adults blindfolded. This indicates that not only is vision highly important in normal balancing, but that little compensation for absence of visual cues is possible for the blind under normal conditions. Others, notably Miles (1950) and Edwards (1946), have shown that in sighted adults body sway increases by as much as 50 per cent to 100 per cent when visual cues are removed. The phenomenon of deteriorating performance following the removal of visual cues has been demonstrated in both static and dynamic balance (Travis, 1945).

Several tests for balance ability have been designed. These tests may be divided into two categories, those involving static body balance and those measuring dynamic balance. Miles (1950) referred to static balance as the equilibratory activity in which the body does not move, that is, in standing, for example. On the other hand, Bass (1939) suggested that static balance consists of equilibratory activity in which the body does not move whilst competent performance is continuing. In this case, standing on a beam or standing on a tight wire would be considered static balance. Dynamic balance is defined by Bass as the maintenance of equilibrium whilst the body is undergoing changes of position. For example, walking along a balance beam would be considered dynamic balance.

The relationship between these two forms of balance has been the subject of some discussion. Travis (1945) showed that there is no significant relationship between the ability of subjects to balance statically (as measured by amount of body sway) and the ability to balance dynamically using an unstable platform. Supporting evidence has come from Graybiel and Fregly (1965) who found no significant correlation in subjects' ability to stand on a narrow beam and ability to walk along a beam, and most recently from De Oreo and Wade (1971). On the basis of this evidence it appears that the necessary sub-components serving these capacities are orthogonal.

The measurement of static balance has taken many forms. Perhaps the most direct technique has employed the ataxiameter (Miles 1950). This instrument designed to measure body sway, consists of a square wooden frame adjustable vertically to the subject's height. The subject stands inside this frame wearing a cap to which are attached four threads leading to four counters set at each corner of the frame. Any head movement is recorded by one or more of these counters. This system then provides a numerical record of body sway. The major function of the ataxiameter has been as a clinical test of diseased or disordered equilibratory function.

Leonard (1966) and Dickinson (1968a) used a different approach for measuring static balance. A beam of variable width was chosen as the apparatus. Subjects were required to stand on the beam and maintain their balance for an arbitrary period of 60 seconds. The narrowest width of beam upon which this criterion was achieved was taken as that subject's score in static balance.

In a further experiment by Dickinson (1968b) several forms of measurement of static balance were compared. Using beam widths varying from ½″ to 4″ the length of time subjects were able to balance was recorded, the amount of lateral sway exhibited by the subject was recorded during balancing and measured by an accelorometer trace. An integrated EMG score was also taken from the invertors and evertors of the rear leg whilst balancing was in progress. The accelerometer was strapped around the subject's chest. Any lateral movement of the body was monitored on an ultraviolet recorder. For the measurement of invertor and evertor muscular activity two integrated scores were used. One was reset electronically every second giving an ultraviolet recording of per second voltage changes. The other was reset electronically when a predetermined change in voltage output occurred. A digital read-out of the number of times the circuit was reset over a specified period of time therefore gave an accurate measure of the input voltage/time integral. Subjects were tested both sighted and blindfolded.

It was found, in general, that there was a high level of correlation between the different techniques of appraising static balance. As the beam width was narrowed, body sway increased, the length of time for which competent performance was possible decreased, and muscular activity increased. There were wide individual differences on all measures taken. Not surprisingly it was found that performance was inferior according to all measures when the subjects were blindfolded.

Because of the greater relevance to many gross motor activities many varied approaches have been made to the measurement of dynamic balance. Three broad categories of techniques are perhaps most common. Firstly, tests involving several types of gymnastic stunts have been employed in measuring dynamic balance in a physical education setting. Secondly, clinicians have tended to use rail walking tests which establish defects or capacity in balancing under conditions of quasi-normal gait. Thirdly, laboratory tests have examined performance in balancing on an unstable platform or stabilometer. Normative data are available concerning performance in dynamic balance both sighted and blindfolded, under the influence of alcohol and after exercise.

A test of dynamic balance, of use only with respect to those with vision, has been devised by Bass (1939). In this test subjects are required to perform a number of stunts which either require the subject to maintain equilibrium during their performance or when the subject has completed a series of movements. A composite score is developed of the subject's capacity to perform those tasks.

Tests of dynamic balance involving the use of beams or rails have also been fairly common. Such a test was standardised by Fisher, Birren and Leggett (1945). A beam, one inch wide and 10 feet long, was used and subjects were required to walk the beam in a heel to toe fashion with the hands behind the back. Performance was measured by the distance covered in ten trials. That is, maximum score was 100 feet. The disadvantage with this test was that it failed to discriminate between those with perfect scores. An alternative was devised by Graybiel and Fregly (1965). In this test 6 different rails were used, each 8 feet long and varying in width from 2½ inches to ½ inch. Their test involved subjects walking along these rails in a heel to toe manner starting on the widest beam. The score was taken as the number of steps made before the subject could no longer maintain his balance. The test was also intended for measurement of static equilibrium. In its measurement of dynamic balance it resembles a much earlier test devised by Seashore (1938).

In 1944 Travis produced an apparatus for the measurement of dynamic balance which he named a stabilometer. This consisted of a platform on a universal joint. Electronic counters measured deviation of the platform by more than 2 degrees from the horizontal. When the platform was in the horizontal position, a stylus was located on a target. The task of the subject was to maintain the stylus on target for a period of 60 seconds. A similar test devised by Begbie (1966) used a rocking platform equivalent to one elipse rolling on another. The subjects' task was to keep the platform as steady as possible in a horizontal position for 60 seconds. The score in this case was the largest deviation between a right and left sway during the middle 40 seconds of the testing period. Begbie pointed out that in these tests in which it is the platform which moves, it may not be permissible to label the activity dynamic balance.

A similar test which did involve dynamic balance was designed by Reynolds (see Slater-Hammel, 1956). In the Reynolds' test, an unstable platform, or teeter board was used. Also required for the test were a stimulus and response display and a timing unit. Any activated stimulus lamp required the subject to move the teeter board to a specified position in order to activate a response light. When the paired lamps had been matched for 0.15 seconds, another stimulus was given. The score was the total time in which a subject could match a cycle of 25 stimulus presentations.

These divergent techniques of measurement have produced generalizations regarding the development of balance ability. Hellebrandt, Braun and Tepper (1937) showed that body sway is endemic to upright stance. They suggested that the function of body sway is that it provides a constantly varying stimulus which could be responsible for the relative indefatigability of postural tone. In addition, constantly varying stimuli may also mitigate proprioceptive adaptation in the postural muscles. Hellebrandt el al also demonstrated that body sway occurred throughout life. Others have looked more closely at the developmental aspects of balance ability.

Much of the developmental research has concerned itself with balance ability between 10 and 18 years of age. The reason for this may be found in the apparent clumsiness of teenagers which has been ascribed by some to deficiencies in balance. Seashore (1938) showed that balance ability increases with age, but that there does appear to be a negative acceleration in balance capacity after the age of 11. No authors report a decrease of ability during adolescence, but many note a slowing of the rate of the development of balance ability (Espenschade et al, 1953; Cron and Pronko, 1957; Wallon et al, 1958). The conclusion, however, has not gone unchallenged. Over an age range of 6 to 26 years, Bachman (1961) found no influence of age and Miles (1950) reported only minor changes. With very young children, increasing performance occurs with age. Using 3, 4 and 5 year olds, age was found to be a highly significant factor in both static and dynamic balance ability by De Oreo and Wade (1971).

Sex differences have been reported in both static and dynamic balancing. In the measurement of body sway various authors have noted the superiority of females. Edwards (1947) claimed that females were significantly steadier than males when standing normally. This was confirmed by Witkin and Wapner (1950). One interesting point demonstrated by Fearing (1924) was that females showed a marked decrease in performance with the onset of menstruation. One reason which has been suggested for the sex difference is the lower center of gravity of females. Height and weight may have an influence on body sway.

In dynamic balance, the evidence is not quite so uniform. Travis (1944) found that females were better at a dynamic balance test than males and in a later study (Travis, 1945) that females recovered more quickly from rotation as measured by their ability to balance. Cron and Pronko (1957) supported this position in younger age groups but found that males were superior after puberty. On the other hand, Goetzinger (1961) and Bachman (1961) could find no difference in dynamic balance ability between the sexes.

Confusing evidence also exists concerning the relationship between height and weight and balance ability. There is an obvious relationship between height and weight and sex, but in same-sex studies some correlation has been noted, depending upon the type of test used. Many dynamic tests of balance (Graybiel and Fregly, 1965; Espenschade, 1953) have failed to find a relationship. Travis (1944, 1945) on the other hand found that in performance of a dynamic test of balance weight was inversely correlated with ability. In his experiments on static balance, however, a negative correlation was found with both height and weight. In another static balance study, Fearing (1924) claimed that both increasing height and weight caused increases in body sway and suggested that height was more important than weight. Agreeing with this conclusion, Miles (1950) suggested that height was the greater influence in the ratio of 4:1. Alternatively, Leonard (1966) and Dickinson (1968b) could find no such relationship in both static and dynamic tests. With a total of 170 subjects differing in height from 5′ to 6′ 4″ and with weights ranging from 8st.5lbs to 15 st., no significant correlation was found between:-

(a)   sighted static balance and height or weight,
(b)   blindfold static balance and height or weight,
(c)   blindfold dynamic balance and height or weight.

In summary, the evidence from studies of balance indicates that this activity is the product of three distinct factors. Firstly, both vestibular and other proprioceptors participate in maintaining equilibrium. Secondly, vision enhances this performance and makes some types of dynamic balance possible, and finally, acquired skill enables the performance of balanced activities.

Proprioception and Body Tilt

In the discussion of absolute thresholds in proprioception the absolute thresholds for recognition of body tilt were discussed. There are, however, other relevant measures of body tilt using proprioceptive cues although a large proportion of measures have involved the use of visual information (Witkin and Wapner, 1950). In the earlier discussion it was noted that many proprioceptive studies of body tilt were confounded by cutaneous sensory information. Howard and Templeton (1966) reported work by Garten (1920) which is instructive. Garten tested subjects with defective vestibular systems and found great accuracy in the ability of these subjects to set a tilting chair to the vertical position, the inference being that vestibular information may not be of paramount importance in the capacity of subjects to perform this task. Similarly, anaesthetizing those areas of the body in contact with the tilting chair had no effect on the ability of normal subjects to place a tilting chair in the vertical position. It was Garten's contention therefore that non-vestibular proprioceptors are the major means by which judgements of the vertical are made in the absence of vision. More recent evidence from both vestibular defectives and normal subjects have provided some contradictory evidence, however (Mann, Berthelot-Berry and Dauterive, 1949; Clark and Graybiel, 1963). It appears from this later evidence that some contribution from both touch and vestibular sources is likely. Solley (1956, 1960), for example, has demonstrated in a rigorous series of experiments that when the head is not in line with the body, that is, when vestibular and non-vestibular sources provide contradictory evidence of verticality, performance is inferior to performance with head and body in line.

The accuracy with which subjects can establish a vertical position in a tilting chair is generally superior with vision. However, practice in non-visual performance produces improvement and performance approaches sighted levels of competence (Kleinknecht and Lueg, 1924). Perhaps the interpretation of proprioceptive cues therefore, initially less accurate, may approach visual accuracy when it is necessary that attention is paid to this sensory source.

Gross Bodily Measures of Proprioception

During the 1950s there was great interest among physical educators in producing a test of total proprioceptive sensitivity which would give a straightforward prediction of the capacity to learn motor skills (see Scott, 1955; Wiebe, 1954; Roloff, 1953). Three major problems faced these investigators. Two of these have already been discussed—the reliability and validity of the measures used. The final problem was the apparent specificity of proprioceptive functions. That is, gross bodily measures of proprioceptive function did not correlate very highly with each other. It was not found possible, for example, to produce a single test which gave an adequate indication of total proprioceptive sensitivity (Scott 1955, Wiebe 1954). Some investigators attempted to produce a combination of tests which would give an overall impression of proprioceptive sensitivity. The adequacy of these test batteries may be measured by the fact that very few studies have ever reported their use in experimentation or for predictive purposes. The test batteries proposed seem mainly to be the product of the fortuitous correlation of individual items with a total score, derived from tests with 'face validity'. For example, Wiebe included in a test battery:—

1   Balance test. Subject standing on one foot on a 1″ wide stick with eyes closed. Scored in seconds.
2   Leg raise test. Subject shown a stick figure with one leg raised to a 20 degree angle from the vertical and asked to replicate. The score was based on errors.
3   Vertical space test. Subject shown a yardstick and asked to close his eyes and point at the 16 inch point. The score was based on errors.
4   Separate feet test. Subject asked to stand with feet together and then required to separate them to a point at which they were 12 inches apart with eyes closed. The score was based on errors.

Roloff (1953) suggested that a 'kinaesthesis score' could be achieved by using the following formula: .75 Balance Score—Arm Raising Score—Weight Shifting Score + 4.7 Arm Circling Score + 50, where balance was measured by stick standing with eyes closed, arm raising by errors in attempting to place the arm horizontal to the ground with eyes closed, weight shifting by ability of the subject to divide his weight equally between the two feet and arm circling was measured by a subjective rating of the subject's ability to circle the arms in opposite directions.

In Conclusion

The diversity of techniques for measuring proprioception has produced a difficult picture to summarise and perhaps any attempted summary is premature. If certain aspects of these measures are emphasized the impression is gained of proprioception as a highly accurate source of information. Gibbs and Logan (1965), for example, stressed that proprioceptive cues are sufficient for exact limb placement. Additional supportive evidence comes from many studies of a psychophysical nature (e.g. Martenuik, Shields and Campbell, 1972). At the other extreme of the continuum, Smith (1969) was convinced that proprioceptive information could only provide a gross representation of movement and man could not perceive details. Alternatively, she suggested perception of proprioceptive cues *could* provide accurate information but man is too oriented toward external cues to attend to and use effectively this form of information. These extreme views are typical of the controversy which surrounds proprioception and the problem is considered again in later chapters.

4

PROPRIOCEPTION AND PERFORMANCE

4 PROPRIOCEPTION AND PERFORMANCE

Introduction

The pheonomenon of proprioceptive feedback is associated with the performance of all physical tasks. Not all of this feedback may be consciously appreciated. However, the evidence presented in the last chapter suggests that for a large range of human movement there is an appreciation of proprioceptive stimuli. In some respects man appears to be highly sensitive to these stimuli, but the multidimensional character of proprioception defies generalization. Since man is capable of detecting movement at a conscious level with some degree of accuracy, a superficial conclusion might be that proprioception is highly relevant to performance. Similarly, the conclusion may be extended to suggest that the greater the degree of sensitivity the more accurate the movement characteristics will be. That is, if proprioceptive ✳ feedback is relevant to skilled movement, the greater the proprioceptive sensitivity, the higher the level of skill with other aspects constant. This proposition has been the basis of much experimental research and the conclusion has found support in many studies. However, this view has not gone unchallenged. The purpose of this chapter is to review the evidence for the role of proprioception in performance and present contrasting points of view in the interpretation of this evidence. The next chapter is more concerned with proprioception and learning.

The distinction between learning and performance can be made at several different levels. Most frequently learning has been defined in terms of relatively permanent changes in behaviour whereas performance is regarded as behaviour which may result from learning, but also be influenced by factors other than learning. For example, fatigue, drugs and other temporary states of the organism are usually viewed as affecting performance rather than learning. However, as Gagne and Fleishman (1959), and Bugelski (1956) pointed out, learning is essentially an internal neural change, and its occurrence must be inferred from performance. The methodological and theoretical problems which this complication has occasioned are considerable.

65

For example, the phenomenon of latent learning described by Tolman (1932) originally, has caused attempts at redefining the concept of learning. Kimble (1961) viewed learning more as a change in the potentiality of behaviour rather than its overt demonstration. Although theoretically significant, this distinction does not provide an answer to the experimental difficulties in distinguishing between changes in behaviour due to factors influencing only performance and those influencing learning.

In this chapter and the next, the role of proprioception in performance and learning is discussed in some detail. It is beyond the scope of this work however to detail the controversies in the distinction between these two phenomena. This chapter considers the role of proprioception in motor behaviour in a static sense. That is, an examination is made of proprioception's role in the accomplishment of a single motor task. Models are presented of the processes involved. It is left for the next chapter to discuss how this role may vary as level of skill increases. The division of material between the two chapters has not been made therefore upon any solid theoretical basis, but has been made for convenience. For example, where experiments purportedly concerned with learning have also illustrated aspects of proprioceptive activity in performance, they have been included in this chapter. After all, learning trials may also be viewed as a series of discrete performances.

Proprioception as an Ability

One of the ways in which proprioception may be viewed as a factor in performance is as an ability in the sense in which Fleishman (1965, 1966) used the term. According to Fleishman, an ability '. . . refers to a more general trait of the individual which has been inferred from certain response consistencies (e.g. correlations) on certain kinds of tasks. These are fairly enduring traits, which in the adult, are more difficult to change. Many of these abilities are, of course, themselves a product of learning, and develop at different rates, mainly during childhood and adolescence.' Fleishman 1966, pp 147-148). Fleishman suggested that some abilities may also be the product of genetic factors. Abilities are thought to underly or be sub-components of specific skills.

This view of the concept of ability is somewhat different from other interpretations. For example, Thurstone (1947) suggested that an ability is a trait which is defined by what an individual can do. According to this definition, of course, there are as many abilities as there are activities. However, by means of factor-analytical approaches the number of abilities may be reduced to a relatively small number of categories. It is really these categories which Fleishman re-defined as abilities. Ferguson (1954) in a discussion of non-genetic abilities, made the observation that abilities are themselves a product of learning. Since, however, abilities are relatively stable attributes in an adult, Ferguson suggested that the term ability is roughly equivalent to an asymptote in learning. That is, '. . . individual differences in ability are individual differences at some crude limit of performance reached by overlearning . . .'

Ferguson and Thurstone were less concerned with motor than with intellectual abilities and did not distinguish between abilities and skills. Skill is considered by Fleishman as a level of proficiency on a specific task, whereas ability may be related to proficiency on several different tasks. Fleishman (1966) used the following example. If an analysis is made of those abilities which contribute to performance in the specific skills of dentistry, blue-print reading and aerial navigation, it is found that the ability of spatial visualization is a component of performance in all three. Thus, the general ability underlies, in this case, three specific skills. Many abilities contribute to each specific skill, and each ability contributes to many different skills. An individual may possess high levels of ability over a wide range, or show high levels of ability in only a small number of contributing factors. In the first case, the subject with superior levels of proficiency in a large number of abilities is likely to produce high calibre performances on a large number of specific skills. Similarly, the individual who has only low proficiency in all abilities is never likely to show high levels of performance in specific skills.

It is perhaps unnecessary to point out that using this type of analysis predictions may also be made concerning the efficiency of learning rather than performance. An individual faces a new learning task equipped with his existing abilities, and his progress in that new task is likely to be determined, in part, by the quality of those abilities. The relevance to learning will be dealt with in greater detail in the next chapter.

In one study, Fleishman and Rich (1963) examined 'kinaesthetic ability'. This was measured by sensitivity to lifted weights. They noted that relatively little was known concerning 'kinaesthetic ability' traits distinguishing one individual from another. Although it was found in this experiment that proprioceptive sensitivity was a useful predictor of performance at later stages in learning, Fleishman does not include proprioceptive sensitivity as one of the major ability traits in his later summaries (Fleishman, 1966).

Fleishman (1966) listed eleven of the important ability traits found by himself and co-workers to underly a large range of physical skills. These eleven abilities produced through factor-analytical studies have been assigned names arbitrarily. However, if the abilities are examined it is apparent that many of them either include as a component or are totally measures of different kinds of proprioceptive sensitivity. The eleven factors follow (from Fleishman, 1966).

1 Control precision: this factor is common to tasks which require fine, highly controlled, but not overcontrolled, muscular adjustments, primarily where larger muscle groups are involved.

2 Multilimb coordination: this is the ability to coordinate the movements of a number of limbs simultaneously, and is best measured by devices involving multiple controls.

3 Response orientation: this ability factor has been found general to visual discrimination reaction psychomotor tasks involving rapid directional discrimination and orientation of movement patterns.

4 Reaction time: this represents simply the speed with which the individual is able to respond to a stimulus when it appears.

5 Speed of arm movement: this represents simply the speed with which an individual can make a gross, discrete arm movement where accuracy is not the requirement.

6 Rate control: this ability involves the making of continuous anticipatory motor adjustments relative to changes in speed and direction of a continuously moving target or object.

7 Manual dexterity: this ability involves skilful, well-directed arm-hand movements in manipulating fairly large objects under speed conditions.

8 Finger dexterity: this is the ability to make skill-controlled manipulations of tiny objects involving primarily the fingers.

9 Arm-hand steadiness: this is the ability to make precise arm-hand positioning movements where strength and speed are minimized; the critical feature, as the name implies, is the steadiness with which such movements can be made.

10 Wrist, finger speed: the ability has been called 'tapping' in many previous studies through the years. It has been used in a variety of different studies, primarily because these are in the form of printed tests which are quick and easy to administer.

11 Aiming: this ability appears to be measured by printed tests which provide the subject with very small circles to be dotted and where there are a large number of circles and when the test is highly speeded.

Of these eleven factors or abilities, control precision (no. 1) obviously relies on proprioceptive information to a very high degree. Similarly, factor no. 2 or multilimb coordination is an aspect of proprioceptive function, other tests of which were mentioned in the last chapter. Abilities 7, 8 and 9—manual dexterity, finger dexterity and arm-hand steadiness—all involve proprioceptive feedback. The quality of this feedback or sensitivity of the subject to proprioceptive stimuli, will determine that subject's level of ability in large measure.

Fleishman and co-workers have spent considerable research effort on examining the relevance of these abilities to specific skills such as driving and pilot flying performance. Their results indicate that this method of examining skill has great value in description of skills and as a diagnostic and predictive tool (Fleishman and Ornstein, 1960; Herbert, 1963).

The majority of the skills and tests with which Fleishman was concerned in these studies were of a relatively fine nature. That is, the tests tended to rely on small scale movements made within the laboratory situation. In 1964, however, Fleishman applied the same factor-analytical approach to gross bodily movements. In an examination of 60 physical fitness tests, eight important factors were identified. These were: extent flexibility, dynamic flexibility, static strength, dynamic strength, trunk strength, stamina, gross body coordination and gross body equilibrium. The last two of these factors are also measures, in effect, of proprioceptive sensitivity. It is clear from the results of these studies that the contribution of proprioceptive sensitivity to performance is highly significant. They also emphasize the fact that proprioceptive sensitivity is highly specific and not a single general factor.

The view which Fleishman took of the relationship between abilities and skill has been criticized from several standpoints. Jones (1966) for example made two salient points. Firstly, as research has increased over the years, the number of factors or abilities which have been identified has grown correspondingly. Jones suggested that there may be an infinitely large number of abilities and that those which have been identified thus far are a function of the tests selected and do not necessarily reflect the abilities of subjects in anything like their entirety.

A further criticism stresses the incapacity of the analysis to account for all the variance found in psychomotor tasks. As Jones (1966) explained: 'In psychomotor tests generally, most of the variance at the end of practice is specific to the task. This finding has tended to focus attention for the first time in many years on specific variance.' (Jones, 1966, p. 144). Jones suggested that for many studies the range of variance found to be specific to the task was between 50 and 90 per cent. The wisdom of accounting for differences in performance when so much of the variance is unexplained has rightly been questioned. Additional criticism of Fleishman's views have been made in a recent review by Alvares and Hulin (1972). Their criticisms are more relevant to the discussion of learning, but their major point is also important in the discussion of performance. They claimed that abilities may not be relatively constant as Fleishman suggested, but be systematically and significantly affected with practice on a specific skill.

Several attempts have been made, however, to investigate specific skills and the degree to which measurement of abilities can predict or determine level of performance. Two studies which have examined this problem with respect to proprioception as an ability are Fleishman and Rich (1963) and

Dickinson (1969). In both these studies, the primary intention was the examination of the interaction between ability and learning, however the results may also be interpreted in terms of performance. In both cases it was found that a measure of weight sensitivity, using the difference threshold for lifted weights, correlated significantly with performance of a motor task at some stage during the acquisition process. In the Fleishman and Rich experiment a two hand coordination tracking task was used, whereas in the Dickinson study the test involved a gross motor aiming task. The results of these studies indicated that it was valid to view proprioceptive sensitivity—in this case as measured by sensitivity to lifted weights—as an underlying ability of the respective skills. Although this ability accounted for perhaps only a small proportion of the variance, the contribution was nevertheless significant.

Several attempts have been made to relate tests of the totality of proprioception to physical performance. Unfortunately the quality of the tests do not allow very significant conclusions to be drawn (see Chapter Three). The example was given in the last chapter of the discrimination between athletes and non-athletes as a measure of validation for tests of proprioception. These results may also be used to indicate that perhaps proprioceptive sensitivity is an ability relevant to athletic performance (for examples, see Kerr and Weinlund, 1933, and Wiebe, 1954). Other experiments have shown similar levels of importance for proprioception in gross motor skill activities. Phillips (1941) and Phillips and Summers (1954) used a single measure of proprioceptive sensitivity, arm positioning ability, and found a significant relationship between this measure and performance at certain stages in gross motor skill activity.

Balancing as an ability related to physical performance

Since Fleishman has noted that balancing is an important factor in gross motor activity and since proprioceptive components are highly important in balancing, it is justifiable to consider balance as an underlying proprioceptive ability in gross motor performance. There has been a considerable number of studies which have attempted to relate balance ability to the performance of physical skills. Perhaps the earliest of these was a study by Burtt (1918). He demonstrated that there was a correlation between the ability to balance and performance in flying. (Whether this would be the case today is open to question). More recently studies have tended to use student groups. Slater-Hammel (1956) showed that balance ability discriminated between athletes and non-athletes. Varsity athletes were found to be significantly better than physical education majors, and physical education majors were superior to liberal arts majors. Espenschade et al (1953) in their studies with adolescent boys noted that balance ability is correlated with performance in those skills necessary in the physical education programme. Estep (1957) also found that there was a correlation between ability in static balance and skill in gross motor activities. Other work has been more specific and examined the relationship between balance ability and performance in a specific skill. Gross and Thompson (1957), for example, considered balance ability an important factor in swimming performance. They used a beam walking test as a measure of balance and had judges rank swimming technique as well as obtaining measures of swimming speed. Their results showed a correlation between both technique and speed with balance ability. In a similar kind of study, Mumby (1953) has shown that proprioceptive sensitivity and balance ability are related to wrestling skill. Some negative evidence does exist. Fearing (1924) could find no relationship between ability to balance and athletic skill.

Proprioceptive Reaction Time

It will be remembered that one of Fleishman's important abilities was labelled as reaction time. This was defined as the speed with which a subject may respond to a stimulus when it appears. The work conducted in the exploration of simple reaction times has generally used visual stimuli requiring motor responses. Reaction times to proprioceptive stimuli are also of obvious importance in performance. The importance of proprioceptive reaction time cannot be over-emphasized since if proprioceptive information is to be influential in the control of small scale and rapid movements, it must be possible for extremely rapid processing of proprioceptive information to result in appropriate responding.

Some of the first experiments on proprioceptive reaction time were those conducted by Hick (1949), and Vince (1948). In these studies, subjects were required to respond to changes in resistance to hand movement. The results of these studies were quite divergent. In one of the studies, (Vince 1948), mean reaction times of 160 m. secs were found; in Hick's (1949) study, a value of 300 m. secs was reported. This apparent discrepancy led Chernikoff and Taylor (1952) to attempt the measurement of proprioceptive reaction time using a novel technique. Reaction time was measured to the proprioceptive stimulus of the subject's arm dropping from a horizontal position where it had been held by an electromagnet. Two techniques of measuring the reaction time were used. In one, the subject stopped the arm falling actively and changes in arm acceleration were used as a measure of reaction time. Secondly, a measure was also made of the subject's speed in releasing a key with the other hand when he noted the change in arm position. The shorter reaction time was found with the arm stop measure, which was

significantly faster than the alternative. Mean reaction time with the arm stop
was.118.9 m. secs, and 152.9 m. secs with the key release system. This range
of proprioceptive reaction times falls within the range of reaction times noted
in other modalities. The study therefore provided greater support for Vince's
(1948) suggestion than for the slower reaction time found by Hick (1949). It
was suggested by Chernikoff and Taylor that perhaps other variables
confounded the result found by Hick. The discrepancy between 160 m. secs
and 118 m. secs from the two studies which are most in agreement
is still relatively great. This discrepancy has not been explained satisfactorily
although two suggestions are offered by Keele (1968). Keele considered that
the discrepancy was most probably a result of the greater degree of
uncertainty concerning the timing of the occurrence of a stimulus in Vince's
study. On the other hand, it could have been that Chernikoff and Taylor were
measuring a spinal reflexive response rather than the time required for the
central processing of a proprioceptive stimulus.

It should be noted that the studies of proprioceptive reaction time which
have been discussed were essentially normative in character. Mean performance and standard deviations are the only data presented by Chernikoff and
Taylor for example. No attempt was made in these studies to relate the
individual differences in proprioceptive reaction time to the performance of
subjects on other skills. So far as the author is aware, this type of experiment
is one which has not so far been performed.

Proprioceptive Control or Motor Programme?

Considerable discussion has centred around the proposition that for some
simple tasks (and some authors have suggested for a large proportion of
motor tasks) proprioceptive feedback is not essential for performance at all.
The assumption is made that after learning, a motor 'command' may be
remembered which on subsequent trials may be repeated without reference to
proprioceptive feedback. The question of reaction time is important here.
Chernikoff and Taylor (1952) came to the conclusion that rapid accurate
movements of which man is capable cannot possibly be under proprioceptive
control since central processing time is too great. To use everyday examples,
the finger movements of a pianist or typist may be.so rapid that transmission
delays in the central nervous system preclude the possibility of sensory
control. An alternative explanation has therefore been offered in terms of the
motor programme.

These movements may be likened to many sports skill situations in which
the movement is ballistic rather than controlled. These movements occur so
rapidly that after the initial impetus little modification is possible on the basis
of either proprioceptive or visual feedback. These learned movements have

been called 'pre-programmed' (Whiting, 1969; Cockerill, 1972). In other words, where speed is too rapid for correction to occur during the ongoing activity on the basis of feedback, it is the motor impetus or original muscular contraction which is learned.

One of the first experiments which highlighted this issue was reported by Lashley (1917). Lashley's studies involved the accuracy of movement in the absence of all proprioceptive information from the limb in question. A subject was tested who had lost all proprioceptive information from leg movements because of injury. The totality of this absence of leg propriocept-ion was demonstrated by the subject's incapacity to perceive passively induced movements. Not only was movement unperceived when passively produced, but the subject showed a complete incapacity to reproduce any such passively induced movement. However, when the subject was allowed to make movements actively, he was found to be perfectly capable of replicating those movements with fair degrees of accuracy. The subject was also capable of detecting errors which he made. Subjective reports of overshooting the target distance were shown to be correct. These results appear to point to two conclusions. The quality of memory for motor commands made on previous occasions is sufficiently high for those motor commands to be repeated subsequently. Secondly, the assumption must be made that there is some central feedback system which can detect differences between a new motor command and the remembered motor command. For simple movements therefore, proprioceptive feedback does not appear to be entirely necessary for accurate performance.

Studies have been performed using normal individuals in whom proprio-ceptive feedback has been artificially disrupted. The results of these studies have been less straightforward. Provins (1958) produced a peripheral nerve block by anaesthetizing the index finger of subjects by means of xylocaine. Subjects were tested for ability to tap the index finger in anaesthetized and non-anaesthetized states. The results of the experiment indicated that only a small decrement in tapping performance (6 per cent) was produced by the removal of proprioceptive information. Superficially this evidence appears to be additonal support for Lashley's position. However, Lashley's subject had no proprioceptive feedback from the limb, whereas in Provins' case subjects may very well have received proprioceptive information from muscular and tendonous sources. As mentioned in Chapter Two however, there appears to be little direct connection between these sensory sources and the cortex. These results have found support in the work of Lee and Ring (1954) and Brown, Lee and Ring (1954) in experiments involving the great toe.

On the other hand, similar types of experiments by Laszlo (1966, 1967) produced very different results. In these experiments the subjects were again required to tap the fingers in the absence of proprioceptive feedback. In this case the proprioceptive disruption was produced by ischemia rather than by

74 PROPRIOCEPTIVE CONTROL OF HUMAN MOVEMENT

anaesthetic. The results of these experiments indicated great reduction in the tapping rate of subjects. These results may also be criticised, on two grounds. Firstly, there may be some loss of efferent efficiency due to the ischemia as well as afferent loss. This may have had an important influence upon motor commands. Secondly, the technique cannot be used without causing pain or at least discomfort to the subject. A firm conclusion, therefore, that decrement in performance is entirely due to the absence of proprioceptive feedback cannot be justified. In Laszlo's second study (1967), she also demonstrated that although a decrement occurred following the application of the nerve compression block, a training effect occurred. Immediately after compression, performance was approximately 65 per cent of normal. After eight training sessions of 40 seconds, performance achieved 89.5 per cent of the normal rate. Although Laszlo showed higher levels of decrement in performance than would be predicted on the basis of Provins' (1958) or Lashley's (1917) evidence, it is possible that this decrement is only temporary and the effect nullified after relatively small amounts of training.

Using a smiliar technique to Laszlo, Merton (1964) reported experiments involving the application of a pneumatic tourniquet to the wrist. Perception of passive movement was found to be totally disrupted by these means. When active positioning was required subjects showed no decrement compared with

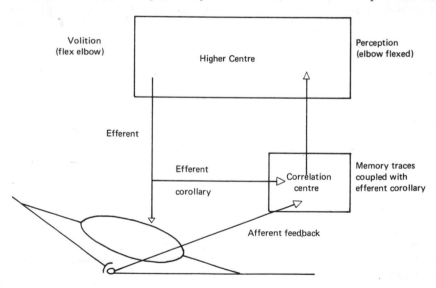

Fig. 7. Schematic representation of Von Holst's model of efferent corollary and afferent feedback correlation and reception for perception (Smith, 1969. In R. C. Brown & B. J. Cratty, eds., New Perspectives of Man in Action © 1969. Reprinted by permission of Prentice Hall, Inc., Englewood Cliffs, New Jersey.)

normal performance. The motor performance of subjects in the absence of proprioceptive feedback, Merton ascribed to the subject's 'sense of effort' or the inner consciousness of the act of producing volitional movement. Smith (1969) has re-interpreted some of Merton's suggestions in the light of a proposal made by van Holst (1954). The system in fact does not differ markedly from that proposed by Ruch (1951) and explained in Chapter Two. Smith (1969) produced a schematic representation of the model which is illustrated in Fig. 7.

In this model any efferent motor impulse is accompanied by a corresponding so-called efferent corollary or efferent copy, which is transmitted to a hypothetical correlation centre. The corollary contains information concerning the characteristics of the movement about to be initiated by the efferent motor impulse. Within the correlation centre (analogous with Ruch's (1951) comparator) the information from the corollary is compared with memory traces of previous movements and the proprioceptive feedback which accompanied them. Under normal conditions there is feedback from the proprioceptors when the movement is accomplished and also feedback from the comparator to the higher centres of movement control. Where proprioceptive feedback is removed there may still be accuracy of movement, provided the memory trace is adequate in the correlation centre. This would account, for example, for Lashley's (1917) finding that a subject was capable of detecting errors in movement in the absence of proprioceptive feedback.

The identification of the higher centre in which this processing occurs is not certain. Perhaps informed speculation has most generally made the assumption that this is a function of the cerebellum. However, higher centres have been suggested (see Smith 1969 for a review). Merton's assumptions contradict some of the evidence which has already been presented.

Gibbs and Logan (1965) in their study cited in Chapter Three certainly found high levels of accuracy in positioning on the basis of proprioceptive information and contended that charges indicating that proprioception is both inaccurate or less than essential are irrelevant and erroneous. On the other hand, Keele (1968) has produced a re-interpretation of some other work of Gibbs (1965) and suggested that motor programming may still be of great importance in the production of skilled movements. In the Gibbs (1965) study it was shown that when subjects were required to make rapid movements in the opposite direction to step function signals on a tracking task, there was a tendency for subjects to initiate movement in the incorrect direction. There was an improvement during practice in the speed with which corrections were made. In the later stages correction time was as low as .11 seconds, which suggested to Gibbs that proprioceptive reaction time rather than visual was responsible. In Keele's opinion an alternative suggestion can be made that '. . . at the appearance of a signal, a motor command is issued to move in the most probable direction. As the signal is further processed, the correct direction is determined and compared with the just issued command, and if there is a discrepancy, a motor command to reverse direction is issued.' On the basis of this hypothesis it is possible that feedback occurs within the central processing areas rather than via peripheral proprioceptive feedback.

Although evidence from studies involving the removal of proprioceptive information do provide good grounds for assuming that some movements may be more under the control of central motor programming and central feedback systems, nevertheless it is likely that in new or complex motor tasks the role of proprioception is high. Even when overlearning has occured, total removal of proprioceptive information may cause severe disruption of performance; for example in the case of the tabes dorsalis patient who has severe problems in achieving normal locomotion, particularly where visual information is reduced (Legge, 1965).

Evidence for the impairment of performance in novel and accurate movements when proprioceptive feedback is disrupted has been provided by Laszlo and Bairstow (1971). In a writing task the application of a nerve compression block was found to disrupt performance significantly. Subjects were trained to write random series of eight letters with the index finger in the absence of proprioceptive feedback. Subjects used either the preferred or non-preferred arm and half the subjects were given practice before proprioceptive information was eliminated. Although hand differences were discovered, the impairment of performance in the absence of proprioceptive information was universal. Surprisingly, a greater reduction in performance was noted for those groups which had practised before the removal of feedback. Laszlo and Bairstow suggested that this was probably due to greater reliance being placed on peripheral feedback for those groups which had practised with feedback. In the absence of proprioceptive feedback improvement did not occur with experience.

Laszlo and Bairstow (1971) reviewed the sum of the evidence concerning the controversy over motor programming and proprioceptive feedback. They identified the following principles. Motor programming of movement and central feedback systems such as those proposed by von Holst (1954) and which are referred to as 'efference copy' feedback systems by Laszlo and Bairstow (1971), are sufficient for the control of *rate* of movement but cannot aid in the control of fine or novel movements. Efference copy feedback systems are also inadequate for improvement in the accuracy of movement.

On the basis of the evidence provided here there are good grounds for accepting the fact that although motor programming and central feedback or efference copy methods of control may be employed in some limited situations, notably where responding is at a high rate or where the response is very simple, the majority of tasks, especially novel ones, require peripheral feedback. Models of possible feedback systems are presented later in this chapter.

The relationship between the characteristics of controls and proprioception's role in performance

An alternative method to the complete removal of proprioceptive feedback has been used in order to elucidate the role of subcomponents of proprioception in performance. This method involves the manipulation of the quality of proprioceptive feedback rather than its complete disruption. By changing the characteristics of controls the kind of proprioceptive feedback made available to the subject can be varied. Resulting changes in performance may then be attributed to the differences in proprioceptive feedback.

In one such study, (Notterman and Page, 1962), a comparison was made between performance on a tracking task using two different types of controls. In one situation, subjects were required to use a movable control stick which had different degrees of elasticity and viscous damping, and in which the control itself had varying degrees of inertia. It was found that performance in this condition was superior to performance with an isometric control in which all three variables were constant. The conclusion therefore was that performance is superior when proprioceptive information arising from applied force as well as from movement is available rather than information from force alone.

Similar experiments were also conducted by Burke and Gibbs (1965), Gibbs (1954) and by North and Lomnicki (1961). In these studies a comparison was made between performance in tracking tasks using isometric pressure on a control and isotonic or movement of a control. In these cases, the results contradict the findings of Notterman and Page in that the isometric pressure condition proved superior. Whilst Gibbs argued that the result indicates superiority of information from isometric contractions, this does nothing to resolve the discrepancy between his results and those of Notterman and Page. Keele (1968) has criticized these experiments of Gibbs (1954), Burke and Gibbs (1965) and North and Lomnicki (1961) on the grounds that the experimental designs do not permit a choice between the following explanations for the results. Keele argued that the results may be due to (1) the fact that preprogramming is more accurate for force than for distance control; or (2) that amplitude controls result in worse performance because it takes longer to make large movements than to make very short isometric movements with pressure controls.

The results of the experiments by Gibbs also contrast markedly with a report by Weiss (1954). In Weiss' experiment the accuracy of positioning responses was tested as pressure and distance information was varied. In this experiment the subjects obtained visual information as well as proprioceptive, but only after a delay. Using 11 different conditions of force-displacement, Weiss found that relative error and variability decrease with distance moved but that pressure variation has no apparent effect on the measures. The effects of variation in distance were found to be greatest at the smallest displacements within a condition. Weiss concluded that in positioning responses where visual feedback is absent, displacement is the more important dimension in the force-displacement relationship.

The conflicting views derived from this kind of study have not been resolved and no firm conclusion is possible. The potential value of these studies in terms of equipment design has maintained interest in the field. It is probable that an explanation of the discrepant results may eventually be made on the basis of confounds between proprioceptive control, motor programming and cutaneous cues. Nowhere are these problems so acute as in the most ambitious of experiments in this field by Bahrick (1957).

Bahrick proposed that by systematically varying the quality of resistance to movement in a control, it should be possible to infer proprioceptive characteristics from the effect upon the subject's capacity to perceive and control his movements. The forces required to move a control, according to Bahrick, can be specified by four physical components of the control: mass, viscosity, elasticity and the degree of coulomb friction. Unfortunately, it has proved relatively difficult to combine all of these factors into a single statement of control effects. For example, Bahrick quoted the following equation based on the work of Howland and Noble (1953): —

$$L_t = K\theta + Bd\theta/dt + Jd^2\theta/dt^2 ,$$

where L_t is the torque required to move the control at time (t)

K is the constant of elasticity of the control,

B is the viscosity constant,

J is the moment of inertia, and

θ is the angular displacement of the control from its centred position.

In this fairly complex equation coulomb friction is still ignored. Allowing for this criticism of the statement, this type of approach has other theoretical as well as practical limitations. As Bahrick pointed out, the forces applied by a subject to a control are only indirectly related to the proprioceptive stimulation he receives. Similarly, the stimulation of cutaneous receptors during application of force may confound the issue further. However, on the basis of the above equation, Bahrick was able to make some predictions concerning the role of proprioceptive stimuli in performance using a control. He hypothesized that man can use the cues obtained in moving a control to improve perception of position, rate and acceleration of limb motion. In Bahrick's terms, 'Specifically it is hypothesized that the elasticity constant of the control improves S's ability to perceive and control positions, the damping constant improves perception and control of rate, and the moment of inertia improves perception and control of acceleration. Thus an increase in each of these control constants should lead to improvement in the corresponding behaviour. At the same time, it is hypothesized that an increase in any of the control constants will affect adversely performance which is aided by the other constants' (Bahrick 1957).

Some studies have been performed which tested the predictions made on the basis of Bahrick's equation. Bahrick, Fitts and Schneider (1955), used a control task in which subjects were required to produce simple patterns of movement with control conditions varying in spring stiffness, damping or mass. After initial practice trials, photographic analyses of spatial and temporal accuracy were made. The results of the experiment indicated that increasing viscous damping or inertia resulted in greater uniformity of speed within individual movements and in successive reproductions of the same movement. The influence of spring loading a control was ambiguous, and in a further experiment Bahrick, Bennett and Fitts (1955), this problem was met by giving extended practice on the use of the spring loaded control. It was shown that positioning errors were smallest when the ratio of relative torque change to displacement was largest. When subjects were tested under conditions of optimal spring loading, it was found that errors in positioning were less than half of those found under a condition with no spring loading.

The review of evidence gathered by Bahrick (1957) supports the hypotheses which were generated on the basis of the equation. The success of the predictions, however, does not circumvent the essential problem with which this approach cannot deal. That is, manipulation of the characteristics of a control and the resulting influence on performance provides, at best, only very indirect evidence of total proprioceptive stimulation and may be seriously confounded by other variables, particularly cutaneous stimulation. In a general review of tracking behaviour, Poulton (1966) commented that an additional problem with Bahrick's analysis is that the arm itself supplies both viscous and inertial resistance, and this has to be added to that of the control. To date it does not appear that this difficulty has been overcome.

In spite of these limitations, Bahrick pointed out the relevant implications in studies of this kind for human engineering. If the characteristics of controls which result in optimum performance can be adequately specified, this is of enormous importance in the design of equipment irrespective of the processes involved.

A Servo-Control Systems Approach to Proprioception & Performance

In the conclusion to Chapter Two, it was noted that proprioceptive activity in control of movements may be conceptualized as a series of interlocking feedback systems. In the course of that chapter, some of the feedback loops, whose physiological characteristics are known, were discussed. It was promised that the topic would be reconsidered at later stages. In this section the general approach to feedback explanations is developed at a theoretical level and some of the models of servo-control systems involving proprioception are examined in some detail.

In 1947 and 1948 Craik published two extremely influential papers. These were, 'Theory of the human operator in control systems. 1. The operator as an engineering system' and 'Theory of the human operator in control systems. II. Man as an element in a control system'. In these papers, Craik discussed the notion that electrical models (his term) could simulate the behaviour of a human operator in motor tasks such as tracking. The analogy between man and servo-mechanisms developed from this point and although the analogy has not been without critics, its development has proved fruitful both in stimulating research activity and in providing descriptions and explanations of many kinds of phenomena associated with motor behaviour. For example, Craik (1947) in an analysis of the errors in tracking behaviour, observed a temporal periodicity of errors. In discounting alternative hypotheses Craik was able to claim that the subject in a tracking task performed in a way very similar to an intermittent correction servo. That is, that man tends to perform tracking tasks by frequent sampling of incoming sensory information and initiation of corrective responses on the basis of the sampling. From this type of analysis there has been developed numerous models of feedback mechanisms which attempt to illuminate the control processes in a skill. The following examples represent a selection of the best known models of feedback in skill, with special reference to the role of proprioception.

By way of introduction, Paillard's (1960) description of the nature of servo-mechanisms is worth noting. 'Components and characteristics of servo-mechanisms are numerous and varied, but their common feature is that they possess some kind of controlling device able to appreciate continuously the discrepancy between the state of the machine realized at a given moment and the final aim assigned to it by its constructor. Through a 'feedback' circuit, the information collected from an error detecting device is at every moment sent back to the servo motor controlling the output. By modifying the input command it permits the output to be corrected for the detected discrepancy. Thus the 'behaviour' of a servo-mechanism is not governed by a blind obedience to the order of a pre-determined program of action, but it presents a kind of self adjustment by modifying the input command of the system as a function of its output.' (Paillard, 1960, pp. 1700).

Perhaps the most familiar of these models is that produced by Welford (1965) which is shown in Fig. 8. Welford (1968) suggested that this was an inadequate model in that only a minority of the feedback loops which exist are shown. Also this diagrammatic model was produced

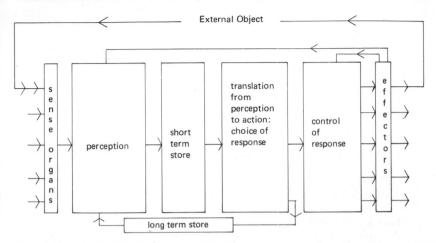

Fig. 8. Hypothetical block diagram of the human sensory-motor system (From A. T. Welford & J. E. Birren, eds. Behaviour, Ageing and the Nervous system. 1965. Courtesy of Charles C. Thomas, Springfield, Illinois.)

by Welford with a more general application than simply the role of proprioception. However, it may be nicely applied to proprioception. The sense organs on the left of the diagram may be thought of as the various proprioceptors contributing to perception. (Perhaps one disadvantage of Welford's diagram is that it does not take account of the sensory information which may influence performance but is not involved in perception). The question of short and long term memory stores with regard to proprioception will be considered in the next chapter. Effector activity then produces a response with a corresponding change in sensory stimulation. It is important to recognize that the feedback loops are not simply the connection between effector activity and changes in sensory stimulation, but in fact feedback occurs at all stages of the process of motor activity.

In an extension of his earlier papers (Gibbs 1954, 1965), Gibbs (1970) produced a paper on the servo-control mechanisms in motor tasks which can be seen as a direct descendant of Craik's early formulations. The models proposed by Gibbs (1970) deal specifically with proprioception and are therefore of great importance in this account. They are based on Gibbs' hypotheses concerning the control of rate of movement and the function of proprioception generally, which were outlined in Chapter Two.

The models were produced with the intention of providing a framework from which the experimental study of transfer of training in skill could proceed, but nevertheless they provide an interesting conceptualisation of performance in its own right. The first of these (Fig. 9) depicts control at the corticocerebellar level and is particularly designed for application in tracking

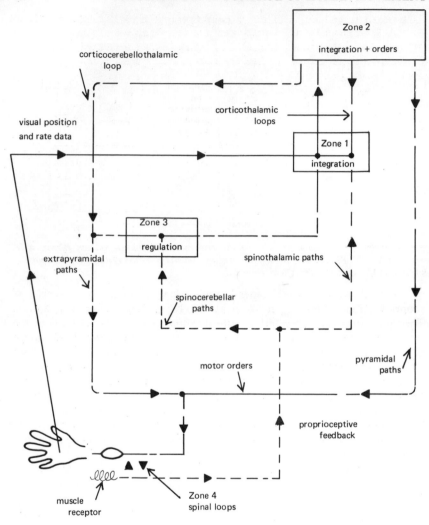

Fig. 9. Diagram of the central nervous system relating to movement control (Gibbs 1970).

tasks. It should be noted that Gibbs has included within his diagram visual as well as proprioceptive information. In this diagram visual information is fed to zone 1 which Gibbs suggested is the thalamus if the translation of the model into physiological terms is made. Zone 1 receives proprioceptive information also and is therefore in a position to integrate the input from these different sources. Zone 1 is thought to produce an error signal which is computed on the basis of the required and the actual position of the limb. The error signal then passes to zone 2 by which Gibbs represented the cortex. Any corrective responses ordered by zone 2 are made via pyramidal and extrapyramidal pathways. The extrapyramidal route also relays information to zone 3 or the cerebellum which in turn receives proprioceptive information. Since zone 3 and zone 1 are interconnected, complete feedback loops are established. This diagram is essentially much the same as that provided by Eccles (1967) and shown in Chapter Two. However, the diagram is noteworthy because of (a) its inclusion of visual input and the way in which this data may be integrated with the proprioceptive feedback and (b) the use Gibbs made of this diagram in presenting a model of the neural arrangements and functions translated into an effective electro-mechanical servo-mechanism (see Fig. 10). Gibbs' description of the model follows. 'The

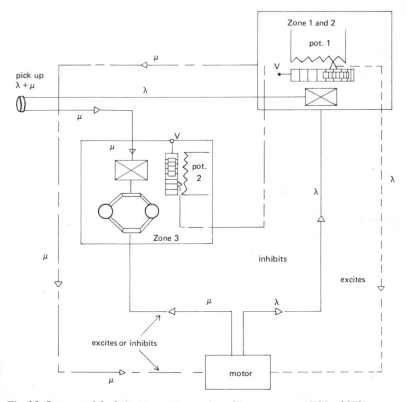

Fig. 10. Servo-model of placing reaction and tracking responses (Gibbs, 1970).

pick-up element (left) detects the position (λ) and speed (μ) of a target. The λ-signal that defines the required position is transmitted to the differential at the upper right of the figure, that also receives feedback defining the actual position of the motor. A rack and pinion moves a sliding contact along potentiometer 1 by an amount proportional to the difference between the required and actual positions of the motor. The motor runs until this difference is eliminated by movements of the λ feedback shaft which return the slider on potentiometer 1 to its zero or null position.

'The required speed (μ) of the system is also detected and transmitted from the pick-up element to move a sliding contact along potentiometer 2. The position of the slider is also affected by a feedback signal defining the actual speed of the motor, that is transmitted via a conventional speed governor. The latter maintains the required motor speed.' (Gibbs, 1970, pp. 217-219). Gibbs suggested that the speed regulator is analogous with zone 3 in Figure 9, or the cerebellum in physiological terms. Similarly the positional differential of the model corresponds to zone 1, or the thalamus. As Gibbs pointed out, the model is highly simplified but nevertheless compatible with some of the data derived at a physiological level. For example, damage to the cerebellum (as noted in Chapter Two) does cause irregularities and incoordination in movement which would also be the result of damage to the

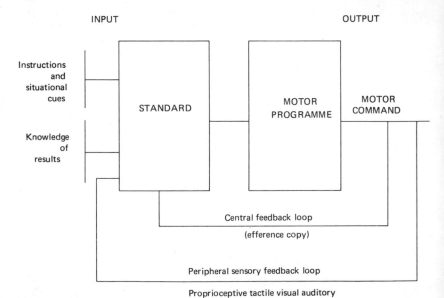

Fig. 11. Model of peripheral sensory feedback loop and central feedback loop with the standard and motor programme units (Laszlo and Bairstow, 1971).

speed regulator in this model. Further, 'The model . . . has a connexion to convey data on the 'present position' of the controlled member to the differential that represents the thalamus. This pathway provides negative feedback that always inhibits movement. The model is therefore consistent with findings that stimulation of the thalamus can halt an animal's movements in a frozen posture.' (Gibbs, 1970, pp. 219).

The most recent of the servo-systems models has been proposed by Laszlo and Bairstow (1971). The model is illustrated in Fig. 11. This model is interesting because it makes use of the evidence reviewed earlier in this chapter concerning the relationship between motor programming and feedback systems. According to this model, the standard is the global memory trace of the task, within which are stored all the data relevant to the task. In Laszlo's terms the '. . . standard forms the central comprehensive percept about the task'. The motor program unit is under the command of the standard and it is this unit which selects the particular motor response which is appropriate on the basis of information provided by the standard. If the skill has been well learned there will be a high quality of information fed from the standard and the most suitable motor commands will be issued. If the skill is entirely new the quality of information fed to the motor program unit will be poor and a relatively lower probability of accurate selection of responses occurs. A sensory feedback loop detects errors in responding. An alternative feedback loop, the efference copy, carries information concerning the nature of the issued command back to the standard. This efference copy contains no information about the results of activity, merely the characteristics of motor output. It was Laszlo's contention that the efference copy loop is sufficient to maintain performance after learning has occurred in relatively simple tasks. Within these simple tasks improvement may also occur in the absence of peripheral feedback. However, where the movement is either complex or novel peripheral feedback becomes essential.

Because the feedback models differ in many respects, it is not possible to consider any of them as being superior. They all offer approaches to the mechanisms involved in skill, which describe certain kinds of motor behaviour with accuracy. Perhaps the ultimate test of the adequacy of these models will come from the physiological investigations of the motor system. With the indirect measurement techniques available in the psychology laboratory it is to be expected that refinements and equally plausible alternatives will be produced.

Information Processing or Communication Models

The control system or servo-mechanism models described in previous pages lend themselves well to a discussion of proprioception's role in performance and particularly the relationship between other feedback systems and proprioception in the total control of movement, but alternative models are available. Rather than viewing motor behaviour as the product of interlocking feedback loops, it is also possible to view this behaviour as information-processing activity guided by some general plan or programme (Fitts, 1964).

Man constantly receives information from his environment. This information arises in the form of stimuli impinging upon his sense organs. At this point, information is transformed into codes which may be thought of as neural patterns of excitation. It is on the basis of these codes of neural excitation that overt responses are made (Fitts & Posner, 1967). The information-processing activities involved are described by Fitts, therefore, as information translation (into codes); information transmission (or the production of a response which bears some fixed relationship to the stimulus); information reduction (as in classificatory or abstracting behaviour); information collation from different sources; its storage and finally the generation of information. Man is able to generate information according to this view since he can store previously received information and use this stored source or memory to amplify incoming information.

This view of skill has been shown to have several distinct advantages. Firstly, information transmission has proved valuable as a means of measuring skills. Skills are so numerous and varied in both their outcome and their physical demands that comparisons from skill to skill are often difficult because of the different measures used. Where information transmission is used the problem is circumvented since the same units of information transmission form the basis of measurement irrespective of the kind of skill involved. To be specific: information transmission is measured by the amount of information contained in the stimulus which is also represented in the subject's response. It is measured in the unit of bits or binary digits (see Attneave, 1959). The rate at which information can be transmitted may also be specified by simply dividing the information transmitted per response by the time it takes to respond. Using measures of this kind, Fitts (1954) and Fitts and Peterson (1964) were able to specify an index of difficulty which could be applied to a variety of tasks enabling comparisons to be made.

An information-processing approach has also been made in the assessment of man's capacities. If man is viewed as a channel for the transmission of information, what are the limits of this channel? Attempts have also been made at examining the transformations which must occur in converting input or stimulus information into output or response information (see Posner, 1966).

Although this view of skilled behaviour has been of great importance in stimulating research in skills, it has been relatively little applied to the role of proprioception in performance. Posner (1967) has examined proprioceptive memory codes in these terms but information-processing in general suffers one salient disadvantage in terms of application to proprioception. One of the greatest merits of information-processing models is the extent to which they permit quantitative analyses to be made. This is only possible where the stimulus or input information is known and is under the control of the experimenter. In proprioception the stimulus is a result of internal activity and is not so easily specifiable. For this reason, the application of information-processing models to the role of proprioception has been difficult. However, Martenuik (1971) has attempted to apply the concept of information transmission in the context of proprioception. He examined the accuracy with which subjects could make absolute judgements concerning the accuracy of movement. For each subject a scale of equally discriminable movements was constructed by having subjects attempt to identify a series of 20 active arm movements by numbers (see Garner and Hake, 1951). Amplitudes for the absolute judgment studies were then chosen from each individual subject's equal discriminability scale. Number of amplitudes was varied under 5 different conditions, in which 4, 6, 8, 10 or 16 amplitudes of movement were used. Each of the amplitudes was assigned a number, and after experience with the assigned numbers, subjects were requested to identify a randomly presented series of movement amplitudes by its assigned number.

Since movement was restricted to adduction of the horizontal arm and speed of movement was regulated, proprioceptive information from the active movement was assumed to vary along a single continuum of stimulation. Where stimuli vary along a single continuum it has been found in other sensory modalities, using informational processing measures, that approximately seven categories of stimulation may be reliably identified on an absolute basis (Miller, 1956). Martenuik (1971) found that when four categories of movement amplitude were used, perfect accuracy was achieved by all subjects (a mean information transmission of 2.0 bits per movement presentation). Information transmission reached a maximum of 2.48 bits of information when 16 categories of movement were used, equivalent to perfect accuracy on approximately six categories. Superficially, these data support evidence derived in other modalities concerning the capacity of man to transmit information when absolute judgments are involved. Martenuik cautioned that certain discrepancies in his results may prove this to be an over-simplification. There was no linear increase in information transmission as number of categories was increased from 4 to 16 as would be predicted from evidence in other modalities. In fact there was a decrease in amount of information transmitted as the number of categories of movement was raised from 6 to 10. Martenuik suggested that these discrepancies may have been the result of changing contributions from different proprioceptive sources. Other stimulus continua may have been involved (another illustration of the problems associated with specifying objectively the stimulus input in studies of proprioceptive perception).

Martenuik's study is important for three reasons. Firstly, it provided evidence that absolute judgments of movement can be made on the basis of proprioception. Secondly, it identified transmission capacities for proprioception and thirdly, it provided a methodological approach for achieving these ends.

Proprioception and vision in performance

Gibbs (1970) introduced the concept of the relationship between visual and proprioceptive systems in performance. In the vast majority of tasks the visual direction of performance appears to be of paramount importance. All movements with an objective external to the organism must require and utilize information derived from the exteroceptors as well as the proprioceptors. The precise way in which the two sets of information are combined is not of course known. However, certain experimental techniques have allowed an approach to be made toward establishing the relative importance of proprioception and vision in controlling behaviour. That vision is the more dominant modality is easily demonstrated in mirror tracing tasks. In this motor skill, subjects are required to trace a star pattern whilst observing their performance in a mirror. Performance in this task is far inferior to performance using direct observation of the hand. The problem appears to be the conflicting sets of information derived from visual and proprioceptive sources. Subjects appear at first to be incapable of resolving this conflict. Since the proprioceptive information is the same whether the subject is using a mirror or not, the decrement in performance seems to be the product of the dominance of visual information. Obviously, the type of skill involved will determine to a large extent the relative importance attached to proprioceptive versus visual information. For example, in many sports skills, the positioning responses must be carried out without visual information, since vision is wholly occupied by tracking a target. Also in many over-learned skills, performance is most usually delegated to proprioceptive control, releasing vision for other purposes.

In spite of these exceptions, it still remains generally accepted that visual control and monitoring of performance is the prime means by which man performs skills. There is increasing evidence that during the course of skill acquisition there may be a delegation of the control of performance to proprioception; but this aspect will be dealt with in the next chapter.

One series of attempts at experimentally demonstrating the relationship between information derived visually and from other sources is described by Rock and Harris (1967). Subjects in one experiment were provided with contradictory information from vision and touch/proprioception. Subjects observed a square through a reducing lens. At the same time they handled the square from below through a cloth base, which masked visual information concerning hand size. Following this procedure subjects were required to either draw the square (a visual and touch/proprioceptive response to the stimulation), or select an equivalent square from an array (visual response), or select an equivalent square from an array which could be handled but not seen (proprioceptive response). The results of this experiment demonstrated very clearly the reliance subjects place on visual information. 'The average size drawn or matched was about the same when the square was both seen and felt as when, in a control experiment, it was only seen. That size was consistently smaller than the size in another control experiment in which the square was only touched. Thus, touch had almost no effect on the perceived size.' (Rock and Harris, 1967, pp. 97). Perhaps the most interesting result here is that even where subjects were allowed to select an equivalent size of square by feeling the squares only, there was still a significant error in performance. It appears from this evidence that where subjects receive contradictory information of this kind, total reliance is placed on the visual system. Interestingly enough, further experiments by Rock and Harris produced the same results for shape as well as size. Objects distorted to look rectangular but which were square, were matched with retangular response stimuli in testing, even after subjects had handled the shapes.

These demonstrations are mainly concerned with touch rather than proprioception *per se*. However, Rock and Harris cited other experiments which are clear evidence that the same phenomenon applies in proprioception. They reported that Hay, Pick and Ikeda (1965) '... had each subject rest one hand on a table and look at it through wedge prisms that displaced its visual image to one side. When the subject was asked to reach under the table and make a mark directly below the fore-finger of his upper hand, a task he could perform quite accurately when blindfolded, he marked a location about as far from the finger's actual location as the prism displaced image.' (Rock and Harris, 1967, p. 99). It is worth pointing out that the test used in the above experiment is one which is very similar to a test of proprioceptive sensitivity (Robinson, 1969).

How does it come about that misperception of proprioceptive and tactual information can occur? The most reasonable suggestion is that tactile and proprioceptive stimuli are quite simply transformed at some integrative level into new tactual and proprioceptive information which conforms with the information being visually obtained. Rock and Harris did not speculate as to the physical location of this transformation. Since the effect is perceptual it is possible that the transformation occurs at cortical levels. However, it may be that integrative procedures at the cerebellum are responsible for matching. If the latter is the case, it would account for the relative permanence of the transformations which Rock and Harris reported. However, if training could remove the effect of the conflicting information one would postulate a higher centre for the transformation. The effect has been well established for a variety of tasks, notably by Rock and Victor (1964).

An alternative approach to the investigation of visual and proprioceptive components in performance was made by Legge (1965). In this case, the drug nitrous oxide in oxygen was administered to subjects prior to participation in the experiment. Subjects performed a positioning task in which vision or proprioception could be used to locate the target and a movable control stylus. Legge used four stimulus conditions where:—

1 vision was used for both target and stylus,
2 proprioception was used for both,
3 proprioception for stylus and vision for target, and
4 vision for stylus and proprioception for target.

It was found that both perceptual condition and nitrous oxide affected the variability in performance of this task, but it was found that the effects of the drug were independent of the perceptual modality. The most interesting result of the experiment was the effects of different combinations of the perceptual modalities. Not surprisingly, the use of vision both for target and stylus produced the greatest precision in performance, that is, greater precision than any condition involving proprioception. However, when vision and proprioception were combined, performance was more variable than when both target and stylus were perceived by the less accurate proprioceptive sources alone. As Legge pointed out, the implication is that the process of integrating information in two modalities results in increased variability in performance. What makes Legge's paper significant is the question mark this places over the traditional view of attributing performance in motor skills to a combination of proprioceptive and visual monitoring. Legge suggested that in light of the evidence from his experiment this position needs to be re-examined. Perhaps the relative decrement in performance as a result of integrating information is simply a fact of life in motor skills. The fact that using one modality alone may cause an improvement in performance is irrelevant since the majority of real-life tasks simply cannot be performed in that way. Alternatively it may be that vision in fact becomes dominant (as would be suggested by the Rock and Harris (1967) work), and proprioceptive stimuli are either ignored or transformed in order to conform with visual information.

It is conceivable that a combination of these two suggestions may also apply. If proprioceptive and visual information are both essential for the task, then the fact that a lower level of performance is achieved than would be achieved with single modality information can neither be tested nor changed. In other tasks, where proprioceptive sources can be ignored without prejudice to performance, this is a likely occurrence. Whilst this speculation demotes proprioception's role in performance it follows logically from Legge's evidence. It is, however, premature to speculate with so little evidence and there are certainly data available which are reviewed in the chapter on training which serve to refute the idea. For example, it has been shown that training in attending to proprioceptive cues can enhance performance. Notwithstanding these data, Legge's point has definite implications in terms of human engineering. The design of equipment should emphasise single modality control where this is possible in order to take advantage of the decreased variability in performance predicted by Legge. It remains to be seen whether the phenomenon generalizes to other motor tasks.

The position taken by Rock and Harris (1967) and to some extent by Legge (1965) contrasts sharply with evidence produced by Held and co-workers (Held 1965, Held & Freedman 1963). Held has conducted extensive investigations into the capacity of man and infrahuman organisms to adjust to displaced visual information. Over periods of time, Held discovered that proprioceptive and motor events played a significant role in producing adaptation to distorted visual feedback.

Experiments dating back to the nineteenth century have shown that subjects wearing distorted prisms are disoriented in motor behaviour. Reaching for objects is highly inaccurate for example. After prolonged exposure, subjects normally adjust and regain original levels of motor coordination. In the past this has been generally interpreted as a product of error correction. Held (1965) disagreed with this proposition and suggested instead that the adaptation was due to the availability of 'reafference'. In brief, reafference is the term applied to neural excitation following sensory stimulation that is systematically dependent on movements initiated by the sensing animal (effectively this means proprioception due to active move-ment). The hypothesis was tested in an ingenious way. Subjects were asked to produce a set of reaching movements with the hand toward target points whilst unable to observe their hands. Subsequently, subjects were divided into three groups. One group observed their motionless hand through a displacing prism. Another group actively moved their hand under the displacing prism for an equivalent period of time and finally, a group observed their hand through the prism being passively moved by the experimenter (see Fig. 12). In the post test subjects were asked to make the unseen reaching movements again. The results of the experiment indicated that significant displacement of the second reaching task occurred for the group which had moved the hand actively, but not for the other two groups. This was seen as supporting the contention that adaptation to distorted vision was a product of reafference rather than a result of error detection. It appeared to be essential for the arm to be moved actively. Passive movement observed through the prism did not produce significant effects on the unobserved reaching task.

Further experiments convinced Held that '. . . the correlation entailed in

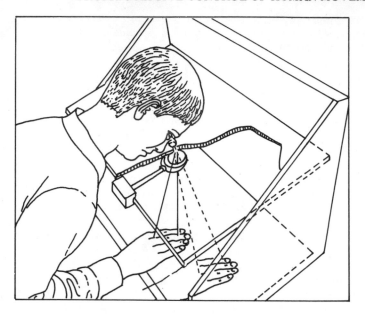

Fig. 12. View through prism displaces a visual image. Subjects either viewed their motionless hand or actively moved the arm or had the arm moved passively (From R. Held. Plasticity in Sensory Motor Systems. Copyright © 1965 by Scientific American, Inc. All rights reserved.)

the sensory feedback accompanying movement—reafference—plays a vital role in perceptual adaptation ... it operates in the maintenance of normal coordination, and it is of major importance in coping with altered visual and auditory inputs.'

Other experimental evidence has been gathered (e.g. by Wallach, Kravitz and Lindauer, 1963) which shows that adaptation may occur as a result of passive exposure rather than the active condition found to be of paramount importance by Held. The position taken by Held (1965) concerning the role of active movement relies in large measure upon the function of motor impulses and their contiguous feedback with proprioceptive stimuli. However, the position has been criticized by Hamilton (1964) who maintained that a more parsimonious explanation may be made simply in terms of proprioception. The fact that there exist differences between passive and active exposure to movement is already established and it is not necessary to postulate any motoric component in order to explain the differences.

There are, therefore, profound discrepancies between the points of view described by Rock and Harris (1967) and to a lesser extent by Legge (1965) on the one hand, and those of Held (1965) on the other. The former authors have concluded that proprioceptive information is at best relatively ignored and may be distorted to conform with visual information. Conversely Held (1965) maintained that proprioceptive cues from active movement are not only fundamental to motor coordination, but are the means by which subjects may adapt to distorted visual information. The positions have not been finally reconciled so far as the author is aware. One possible line of investigation is suggested by the work of Hay and Pick (1966). They reported a series of experiments on the effects of long-term optical displacement. Their conclusion was that adaptation appears to occur in both the visual and the proprioceptive systems. However, proprioceptive adaptation is rather rapid compared with visual adaptation. When visual adaptation does occur it is more permanent in nature. 'The visual adaptation appears to replace an initial, quick acting proprioceptive adaptation during long-term prism exposure.' (Hay and Pick, 1966). It may be better therefore to regard both proprioceptive and visual systems as being equally subject to distortion, the differences found between them being a function of temporal factors in experimental design rather than fundamental differences in dominance.

Proprioceptive After-effects

A related field of study has considered proprioceptive figural or spatial after-effects. Whereas the studies concerning conflicting information between modalities have tended to emphasize distortion occurring as the result of conflict, the studies of proprioceptive after-effects have involved distortion in the interpretation of proprioceptive feedback as a function of subjects' experience of different proprioceptive stimulation. An example will clarify the point. If both arms are raised forward until estimated as being horizontal to the floor, there will be good correspondence in the accuracy of positioning between the arms, even without the help of vision. If one arm is now raised to 45° to the horizontal and maintained in that position for approximately a minute, and subsequently a non-visual attempt is made to re-align the arms in the horizontal position, it will be found that the arm which had been raised will be some 5° or 10° above horizontal. This positional after-effect is therefore a distortion in the interpretation of proprioceptive feedback produced by preceding proprioceptive stimulation.

After-effects are found in other modalities, of course, and have been investigated particularly in vision. According to Charles and Duncan (1959) there appears to be some similarity between the after-effects found in proprioception and vision, but some differences do exist.

The experimental analysis of the phenomenon is based on paradigms used by Gibson (1933 and 1937). These involved exposing subjects to an initial stimulus and then measuring response on a test stimulus. Differences between a group with this prior experience and one which is exposed to only the test stimulus provide a measure of the existence and magnitude of the after-effect. For example, a test stimulus block one inch wide may be held by the subject between thumb and forefinger of the right hand while blindfolded. The thumb and forefinger of the other hand are moved over a wedge shaped block until they are judged to be the same distance apart as the digits on the test stimulus block. Measurement of errors over repeated trials gives an indication of a subject's accuracy in this situation. Subsequently, subjects may be given a stimulus block two inches wide to hold in the right hand. After a period of time holding this block, the right hand is transferred to the one inch test block and the subject required to estimate the width with the left hand on the wedge. Typically it is found that after exposure to a block wider than one inch, the width of the test block is underestimated and conversely where the inspection block is narrower than one inch, the width of the test block is overestimated.

A number of studies have shown that proprioceptive after-effects are not limited to small scale manipulations. For example, Hutton (1966) and Cratty and Hutton (1964) reported after-effects in walking. In the former case, Hutton showed that walking on a gradient produced an after-effect related to gradient. Cratty and Hutton (1964) found that after subjects had been required to walk along curved pathways they reported straight pathways as being curved in the opposite direction.

Cratty (1967) also noted that proprioceptive after-effects are quite common phenomena in sports activities. After trampolining for example, jumping from a solid surface appears subjectively to be impaired. The phenomenon may also be used in order to apparently enhance performance. The baseball batter frequently swings two bats or a weighted bat prior to his turn at the plate; the after-effect presumably serving to make the regulation bat seem lighter. Runners have frequently been reported wearing weighted shoes perhaps for similar reasons. The degree to which this behaviour has a measurable effect upon performance is not clear.

There have been several attempts at identifying the variables which influence the magnitude of the after-effect. One factor which has received considerable attention is the length of time for which the subject is exposed to the stimulus. This 'satiation' time has been found to influence the magnitude of the after-effect. The optimum amount of time appears to vary with the muscle groups involved and the type of movement. Using the finger block method, Bourne and Beir (1961) found that the effect increased to a maximum after between 30 and 60 seconds exposure to the inspection block. On the other hand, Hutton (1966) reported maximal perceptual distortions after 90 seconds exposure in a walking test. Other temporal factors are also important. After-effects appear to be greatest immediately after satiation and the magnitude of the after-effect increases with repeated exposure to the inspection stimulus (Charles and Duncan, 1959). It has also been demonstrated that following satiation there is a gradual decrease in the magnitude of the after-effect, although relatively permanent 'residual' after-effects were reported by Wertheimer and Leventhal (1958) after high levels of satiation.

Obviously subjects must be aware of the initial or inspection stimulus in order for an after-effect to occur. The degree of awareness has been manipulated experimentally by distracting subjects during the inspection of the initial stimulus. Corah and Cohen (1961) reported that if a subject's attention is distracted from an object during inspection, the resulting level of satiation is reduced. This quality of attending to the stimulus may also be influenced by the manner in which the stimulus is presented. Bakan and Weiler (1963) showed that significant differences in after-effects occurred as a result of the subject being passive or active in the inspection phase. This result could be interpreted in terms of either attention or in terms of different tactual and proprioceptive satiation under the two conditions.

5

PROPRIOCEPTION
AND
LEARNING

Chapter

5 PROPRIOCEPTION AND LEARNING

Introduction

The difficulties involved in distinguishing between learning and performance have already been mentioned. Although no extensive consideration was given, it was pointed out that learning is a factor, but not the only factor, in determining level of performance. Discriminating between these two aspects of behaviour, however, is only a first stage in defining learning. Learning must also be distinguished from what Hilgard and Bower (1966) have called 'native response tendencies'. Behaviour which is a product of genetic programming and uninfluenced by environmental factors cannot be included in the definition of learning. Reflexes and taxes are unlearned behaviours which depend primarily on the structure of the nervous system and the physiochemical make up of the organism rather than being the product of learning. Behaviour may also appear as a result of the maturation of the organism or equally be modified by senescence. These changes in behaviour cannot be interpreted as learned. Whilst this negative approach has some advantages, detailing what the term does not include is only a partial answer to the nature of the phenomenon.

Kimble (1961) distinguished between 'factual' and 'theoretical' definitions of learning. The factual definitions are those which relate learning to physical and measurable events in the real world. Thus, learning is considered an intervening variable which links observable independent and dependent variables. Kimble produced the following analysis.

Suggested independent variables:		Suggested dependent variables:
Repetition		Trends in behaviour
Activity		Changes in behaviour
Behaviour		Incremental modification of behaviour
Practice	Learning	
Training		
Observation		
Experience		

The definitions which interpret learning in this way are essentially operational—what Staats and Staats (1963) called 'weak' definitions. They refer to no more than the observations to which they are attached and do not attempt an explanation of the phenomenon of learning. They are, in fact, descriptive rather than explanatory. Further, the analysis presented by Kimble (1961) may not be entirely appropriate in considering motor behaviour. The implication of 'incremental modification' is that learning refers to some kind of improvement in behaviour. This point is also made by Munn (1955) and Thorpe (1956), the latter speaking of 'adaptive changes' as being characteristic of the learning process. As Knapp (1963) pointed out, however, bad as well as good behaviours may be learned in motor tasks. Non-adaptive or decremental changes in behaviour may be a product of learning. Provided this point is borne in mind, the summary comprehends the operational attempts at learning definitions.

The alternative to the operational definitions is the use of theoretical, or in 'Staats and Staats' (1963) terminology, 'strong' definitions. These are definitions which attempt to explain learning rather than simply describe it in observable terms. These definitions show far less similarity than the factual definitions since they reflect each author's personal bias or conceptualisation of the processes involved. Contiguity theorists such as Guthrie (1952) emphasised the temporal relationship between stimuli and responses as a fundamental basis of learning. On the other hand, those who credited reinforcement with a dominant role in learning (for example, Hull, 1952, and his followers) have been concerned that this element should be included in their definitions. Other explanatory definitions have relied on speculation concerning internal or neural activity in the learning process; an explanation of the characteristics of the intervening variable in physiological terms. These definitions stand in marked contrast to the view of the cognitive concepts of learning which constitute yet more theoretical definitions, but ones which stress the reorganization of the perception of the environment by the learner. Perhaps some examples would clarify this issue. A useful operational definition was given by Morgan and King (1956). 'Learning . . . is any relatively permanent change in behaviour which occurs as a result of experience or practice'. No attempt is made to explain the phenomenon. A slightly more explanatory approach was taken by Gagne and Fleishman (1959). 'Learning is defined as the internal neural process assumed to occur whenever a change in performance, not due to growth or fatigue exhibits itself.' Although not a strong definition, the locus and nature of the intervening variable is described. These definitions contrast markedly with the following, which show strong theoretical biases.

For the contiguity theorist Guthrie (1952) learning occurs in this manner 'a combination of stimuli which has accompanied a movement will on its recurrence tend to be followed by that movement'. For Guthrie, therefore, the classical conditioning paradigm forms the basis of all learning. In the law of effect proposed by Thorndike (1898) the results of the action will determine whether or not it is learned. That is, reinforcement is assigned an important function. The law of effect states that 'of several responses made to the same situation, those which are accompanied or closely followed by satisfaction to the animal will, other things being equal, be more firmly connected with the situation, so that, when it recurs, they will be more likely to recur; those which are accompanied or closely followed by discomfort to the animal will, other things being equal, have their connections with that situation weakened, so that, when it recurs, they will be less likely to occur. The greater the satisfaction or discomfort, the greater the strengthening or weakening of the bond.' (Thorndike 1911). It was from this basis that reinforcement theories of learning in the connectionist tradition really began. The works of Skinner, Miller and Hull can all be traced back to this law of effect.

At the physiological level strong definitions may be found in the work of Bugelski (1956). 'Learning is the process of the formation of relatively permanent neural circuits through simultaneous activity of the elements of the circuit-to-be; such activity is of the nature of change in all structures through growth in such a manner as to facilitate the arousal of the entire circuit when a component element is aroused or activated.' More briefly Hebb (1966) noted that 'learning means a change in the direction of messages in the C.N.S.'

The foregoing selection of definitions indicate an unpreparedness on the part of psychologists to agree on any single view of learning. Fortunately, it is not necessary for concensus to be achieved in the discussion of experiments in learning, since there would be a close relationship between psychologists in the identification of experiments in the field. As Hilgard (1951) suggested, 'a precise definition of learning is not necessary, so long as we agree that the inference to learning is made from changes in performance that are the results of training or experience, as distinguished from changes such as growth or fatigue and from changes attributable to the temporary state of the learner. The experiments themselves define the field ostensibly'—a useful summary of the value of operational definitions.

Proprioception and Learning Theory

Throughout its history, psychology has been concerned with the way in which organisms learn. It would not be an exaggeration to claim centrality for learning theories in psychology. The capacity of any theory of psychology to account for the phenomenon of learning has in some measure been an indicator of that theory's quality. Although the great debates between the schools of psychology prevalent in the thirties and forties have considerably dissipated, learning has retained its fundamental role in the totality of psychology. The reduction in theoretical rivalry does not signify a solution of problems, however, and no single theory of psychology nor even single theory of learning can be said to have achieved even partial acceptance amongst all psychologists. The divisions between theories remain and the search for unequivocal crucial experiments goes on.

Hilgard and Bower (1966) list the major issues upon which learning theories divide us:

1 General issues producing a cleavage between stimulus-response and cognitive theories.
   (a) 'peripheral' versus 'central' intermediaries (in other words, cognitive theorists have inferred central brain processes in accounting for behaviour whereas stimulus-response theorists have preferred the view that chained muscular responses are the intermediaries which integrate behaviour).
   (b) acquisition of habits versus acquisition of cognitive structures.
   (c) trial and error versus insight in problem solving.
2 Specific issues not confined to the major families.
   (a) contiguity versus reinforcement
   (b) learning as jumpwise or by small increments
   (c) one or more kinds of experience
   (d) intervening variables versus hypothetical constructs.

(Hilgard and Bower, 1966, pp. 8-13).

For some learning theorists, proprioception has been accorded a major role. Notably, S-R theorists who have accounted for learning on the basis of peripheral intermediaries, have devoted attention to the phenomenon of proprioception (see point 1(a) of Hilgard & Bower, 1966). For example, proprioceptive information is an essential component of the learning theory of Guthrie (1952), whose work has considerable bearing upon the contentious issue of contiguity versus reinforcement mentioned by Hilgard and Bower (1966).

Guthrie's view of learning was detailed in the discussion of definitions of learning. It was his view that modification of behaviour occurs because stimuli come to elicit a response which they had previously not produced, due to the simultaneous occurrence of those stimuli with a response. Obvioulsy, this view of learning applies very well to classical conditioning where an unconditioned stimulus elicits an involuntary unconditioned response and repeated pairings of a conditioned stimulus with the unconditioned stimulus eventually result in a conditioned response to the conditioned stimulus alone. The explanation of instrumental conditioning, in which responding is emitted rather than elicited, is somewhat less clear. However, although there may be no easily identifiable single stimulus in the instrumental situation, the organism is still being inundated with sensory information from the environment. These stimuli may not be manipulated by the experimenter but may nevertheless act as conditioned stimuli analagous to the classical conditioned stimulus. Guthrie (1952) included within these stimuli in instrumental learning situations, the proprioceptive stimuli arising from movement of the organism. It is the contiguous association of these stimuli and the response which causes the development of S-R bonds according to Guthrie. Guthrie (1952) traced his thinking on these matters to William James' (1890) *Principles of Psychology* in which James observed that 'what instigates each new muscular contraction to take place in its appointed order is not a thought or a perception, but the sensation occasioned by the muscular contraction just finished'. Guthrie amplified this point, contending that the stimuli arising from proprioceptors had been neglected simply because they are in a sense 'private' to the stimulated organism. In Guthrie's terms, this neglect is unwarranted since '. . . the continuity of behaviour is largely dependent on proprioceptors. Through them behaviour is coordinated and what is happening in one part of the body is adjusted to what is going on elsewhere.' In this context, therefore, both exteroceptive and proprioceptive stimuli which are present as the response occurs are the 'future cues for the response'. In an instrumental conditioning situation we may not be able to identify the conditioned stimuli, but view them as hypothetical constructs. For example, in a Skinner box, the rat may make a series of movements resulting in proprioceptive stimulation and this pattern of stimulation may serve as a conditioned stimulus. For this reason, Deese and Hulse (1967) observed that according to S-R contiguity theory, any separate discussion of classical and instrumental conditioning is only for the sake of convenience. The distinction between the two kinds of conditioning may even have important disadvantages since it may divert research endeavour from seeking the relevant stimuli in instrumental conditioning.

Two further points concerning contiguity theory need to be made. Firstly, only a minor function is ascribed to reinforcement. Contiguity is the only necessary prerequisite. The effects of reinforcement are, according to Guthrie, influential in behaviour but only since they prevent 'unlearning' of behaviour, e.g. escape from a noxious stimulus which is regarded as being a significant reinforcer in other theories is suggested by Guthrie to operate merely in the protection of previous learning by changing the organism's environment, so that no new responses can be made. Secondly, contiguity theory holds that learning is an all-or-none affair (see Hilgard and Bower's point 2(b) noted earlier). This saltatory characteristic appears superficially to deny all the evidence which shows incremental improvement based on the traditional negatively accelerated learning curve. The explanation given by contiguity theorists is that any response involves many different sub-responses related to an equally large number of stimulus patterns. Each of these sub-responses may be learned in an all-or-none fashion, but it takes a considerable number of trials for the whole pattern of component responses to appear. Therefore, response strength appears to develop by stages. This explanation of the incremental nature of learning has formed the basis of statistical learning theory (Estes, 1959).

In later revisions of his theory (Guthrie, 1959) Guthrie suggested that not only must stimuli and responses be associated contiguously in order for learning to occur, but the organism must be paying attention to the particular stimuli. That is, the organism must notice the stimulus pattern before the association occurs. Because of this revision, Guthrie modified his basic principle to 'what is being noticed becomes a signal for what is being done'.

Since Guthrie's final statements in 1959, considerable research has been devoted to the concept of attention. The subject is reviewed in greater detail later in this chapter. However, it is worth observing that Guthrie's remarks point up the significance of selective attention to both proprioceptive and exteroceptive cues in the learning process (for more extensive treatment of contiguity theories of learning and the criticisms of Guthrie's exposition, see Marx 1970, and Hilgard and Bower, 1966).

The role of proprioception in learning theory has not been exclusively the province of the contiguity theorists. Hull (1952), the most ambitious of the connectionist theorists, emphasised the incremental nature of learning and stressed the role of reinforcement in the learning process. It was Hull's view that stimulus response connections acquire strength as a function of reinforced trials. In dealing with behaviour which involved sequences of action, Hull maintained that a behaviour chain is established by means of exteroceptive stimuli becoming associated with responses, but '. . . the chain does not become fully integrated until the proprioceptive stimuli arising from the animal's own muscles in the performance of one behaviour link serve, at least in part, to evoke the succeeding behaviour link, and so on . . .' (Hull, 1952, pp. 158). The connectionist view of Hull does not differ significantly in this narrow context from Guthrie's position. Both regard proprioceptive stimuli as having the potential to become linked with overt responding. The difference between the two views may be summarised by noting that Hull considered reinforcement essential for the strengthening of this association, whereas contiguity of stimulus and response were sufficient in Guthrie's estimation.

Greater refinement was made to Hull's view of proprioceptive influence in the work of Mowrer (1947 and 1960) who has been most often described as a connectionist in the Hullian tradition, but with 'cognitive leanings'. In the original version of his two-factor theory of learning, Mowrer (1947) distinguished between sign learning and solution learning. In brief, sign learning consists of classical conditioning (in which any stimulus paired with an unconditioned stimulus (UCS) may act as a 'sign' for the impending UCS). Solution learning is the equivalent of instrumental conditioning of responses which reduce drives. The former mainly involves the involuntary responses of smooth muscles and glands; the latter the voluntary responses of the striped muscles. In 1960, Mowrer revised his two factor theory and in an often complex treatise, argued that perhaps all learning may legitimately be called sign learning. Note that this brings Mowrer's position very much closer to the view expressed by Guthrie. However, Mowrer (1960) was very concerned with the role of reinforcement in sign learning (maintaining his connectionist orientation) and particularly made use of the concept of secondary reinforcement. Secondary reinforcers are those stimuli which having been temporally associated with primary reinforcers such as food or release from suffering, acquire reinforcing properties over time. It is in this context that Mowrer extended an earlier argument of Spence (1947) and made use of the concept of proprioceptive feedback. He suggested that these stimuli could come to have reinforcing properties of their own. '... Responses become "habitual" by virtue of the proprioceptive and other stimulation associated therewith having acquired secondary reinforcement value'. (Mowrer 1960). On this basis, Mowrer argued that the 'habit strength' of a particular response depends, not upon the degree of connection at a neural level between the drive and the drive reducing response, but upon the amount of secondary reinforcement developed through association of such 'incidental' stimuli as proprioception with primary reinforcers. The supportive evidence for this position quoted by Mowrer takes the form of analyses of behaviour under conditions of distorted feedback of various kinds. His argument is that drive reduction theory cannot account for the disorganization of behaviour which occurs when feedback is disrupted. That is, if neural connections exist between drive and drive reducing responses why should disruption of the feedback cause disorganization of the responses? For example, if speech is recorded and auditory feedback delayed a short period of time, speaking becomes extremely difficult. This effect cannot be explained by traditional S-R theorists since speech is a highly over-learned habit. Mowrer (1960) reflected that: 'In advancing a feedback conception of both response inhibition (punishment) and response facilitation (habit), we have emancipated behaviour theory from what may be called the 'bondage' of Thorndike's scheme and also liberated it from the crass reflexology of Pavlov'.

Whilst the explanations of habit which invoke 'incidental' stimuli as secondary reinforcers provide answers to the problems posed by experiments on feedback distortion, there is evidence concerning proprioception which appears, superficially at least, to question the generality of the phenomenon. Lashley and McCarthy (1925) demonstrated that a well established habit need not necessarily be disrupted by the severest distortion of proprioceptive and tactile feedback. In one experiment rats learned to run a maze. Subsequently, cortical ablations were performed which prevented the rats from using a normal gait. The rats were then re-introduced into the maze and showed only minor decrements in performance even though movement patterns were totally different and hence proprioceptive feedback must have been completely changed. Mowrer (1960) contended that this discrepant evidence could be satisfactorily explained on the basis of other incidental cues in the environment. In other words, visual, olfactory and other stimuli were still present and the habit maintained on the basis of these secondary reinforcers rather than on the basis of proprioception.

Although Mowrer made considerable use of feedback mechanisms in his theory of learning, it was an incorporation of evidence concerning feedback into a traditional learning theory approach. The concept of feedback has proved so compelling that a completely new approach to learning theories has found its basis in feedback concepts. Cybernetics or behavioural cybernetics, developing from control systems analyses during World War II, found its first coherent expression in Wiener's (1948) book entitled simply *Cybernetics*. The application of cybernetic principles to learning has received its major impetus from Karl Smith (Smith, 1962; Smith 1966; Smith and Smith, 1966). Smith's analyses of the effects of delayed and distorted feedback have led him to far different conclusions from those of Mowrer, and in fact compared with any traditional S-R theorist. Like Mowrer the majority of S-R theorists have accorded feedback reinforcing properties of various kinds, assuming that feedback gives both information and knowledge of results which may also have rewarding properties (see Smith, 1966, for a review). Smith condemned this viewpoint and suggested that many of the problems of learning theories may be solved by abandoning learning theories based on S-R connections and the concept of reinforcement. For example, he claimed that differences between categories of learning, such as classical or instrumental conditioning, verbal learning, problem solving and motor learning are necessary categorisations only because of the inadequacy of association or reinforcement learning models. 'From a cybernetic point of view, the different forms or variations in learning reflect differences in patterns of feedback control which the animal or human subject can utilize in a particular learning situation . . . In this view, the different types of learning result from variations in the modes, conditions, and transformations of feedback stimuli from postural, transport, manipulative, and receptor movements involved in different learning situations.' (Smith, 1966). Within learning as a whole, Smith considered proprioceptive feedback valuable as one source in a multi-dimensional feedback array. However, in order to elucidate the role of feedback in performance and learning, Smith has consistently used delay and distortion of visual and auditory feedback alone. So far as the author is aware, Smith did not attempt the distortion or delay of proprioceptive stimuli. Therefore, the analyses which Smith presented of feedback influences provide no clear information concerning proprioception. Essentially, Smith's many experiments may be viewed not as experiments in feedback delay and distortion *per se*, but as experiments in feedback conflict. That is, the experiments constitute investigations in which visual and/or auditory feedback conflicts either spatially or temporally with proprioceptive and tactual feedback. Smith's assessment of the implications of his work for learning theory has also been criticised by Attneave (1966). Attneave pointed out that Smith has accurately identified the shortcomings of traditional associationist views of learning, by no means a unique feat, but has not satisfactorily replaced it with a cybernetic theory. The evidence produced by Smith and his interpretation of it: '. . . does not constitute a theory . . . because it leaves the formal nature of the learning process unexplained' (Attneave, 1966). Attneave also argued that although Smith's position may be drastically opposed to traditional S-R associationist theories of learning, it may have some communality with the cognitive theories of Tolman (1932) or Miller, Galanter and Pribram (1960).

Adams (1968, 1971) reviewed the traditional S-R associationist views and came to similar conclusions as Smith (1966). Adams was particularly concerned with the role of proprioception. He detailed the associationist conception of proprioceptive feedback acting as a stimulus to respond and suggested that S-R chains of behaviour in which proprioception acts as the stimulus do not account for the following kinds of evidence:

1   In maze learning, rats showed little impairment of performance when proprioceptive feedback was surgically removed (Lashley and McCarthy, 1926). Similarly, Honzik (1936) demonstrated that when all other sensory modalities were obliterated, proprioceptive cues alone were insufficient for maze learning to occur.

2   In classical conditioning, a conditioned response is maintained despite the removal of proprioceptive feedback after conditioning, although qualitative aspects of the response were changed (Taub, Bacon and Berman, 1965; Taub and Berman, 1963). Knapp, Taub and Berman (1963) were also able to establish conditioning in deafferented limbs.

3   Discriminative learning of classically conditioned responses can occur in the absence of proprioceptive feedback (Solomon and Turner, 1962).

Adams' (1968, 1971) papers are again useful in drawing attention to the inadequacies of the major learning theories in their use of the concept of proprioception as an intervening variable or hypothetical construct. As an alternative, Adams proposed a 'closed loop' theory of motor learning in which he stressed that feedback from a response does not act simply as a stimulus for a subsequent response but is compared within a reference mechanism to a desired value of feedback. Discrepancies between feedback and the reference value become the source of error correction. In order for this system to operate, Adams (1971) postulated two independent memory functions. The first of these he called the perceptual trace. This is the memory of the feedback associated with a specific movement in the past against which incoming feedback is compared. It is likened to a proprioceptive/tactual image of the movement. The start of a movement causes the arousal of this perceptual trace and the incoming feedback is then compared with this 'image' and necessary corrections made for any deviation. The acquisition of the perceptual trace is a function of experience and grows in strength with each trial on which the response is produced accurately.

Whilst this account may identify the components of high level performance, it cannot account for learning of course, since the feedback associated with trials early in learning is likely to be erroneous. In other words, the perceptual trace cannot be developed while errors of movement are still being made. Adams (1971) contended that during the early stages the subject uses knowledge of results provided by the experimenter to make his subsequent responses different from the preceding erroneous one. The subject uses the perceptual trace in relation to knowledge of results. When the correct trace has been established, learning consists of its strengthening by successive replication. Although Adams did not use the term he is essentially considering overlearning at this point.

The perceptual trace is the reference mechanism by which the ongoing activity is monitored. A second memory mechanism, the memory trace, is postulated for the initiation of the movement. The memory trace's role is to select and initiate the response, presumably from a store of alternative responses. Once initiated the role of the perceptual trace becomes important. Unfortunately Adams is ambiguous in describing the means by which the memory trace is developed. He suggested that, 'the memory trace must be cued to action and the strength of it grows as a function of practice trials. Strength is a function of stimulus-response contiguity.' It is difficult to decide exactly what is meant by this statement. It could simply mean that the learning occurs without any reinforcement being necessary, but other interpretations are possible. For example, if there are varying time intervals between the stimulus and response, Adams may be claiming that closer temporal proximity leads to greater increments in response strength. Since he did not present evidence, the point cannot be clarified at this juncture.

Adams considered the two memory states as analogous with the difference between recall and recognition in verbal retention studies. The perceptual trace is a process of recognizing response-produced stimuli whereas the memory trace is involved in the recall of a response.

Changes in the Importance of Proprioception during Learning

In 1964, Fitts criticized many of the servo and control system models of performance reviewed in the last chapter on the grounds that they conveyed a static view of the processes involved in skill. By this, Fitts meant that a model which does not change its characteristics as a function of experience, fails to describe one of the fundamental aspects of skill. Performance changes through learning are not simply quantitative but depend also upon qualitative changes. The process of skill learning is dynamic and a model which does not reflect the adaptive nature of the learning process cannot be an adequate description. In Fitts' view, adaptive system models may provide an answer to this problem. By investigation of adaptive feedback systems, artificial intelligences or stored-programme computers which modify their own programmes, it is possible that a more accurate description may be achieved.

One of the alternative methods of investigating changes which occur in learning is to examine the relative importance of different underlying ability traits in the performance of a skill at successive stages during the learning process. The most familiar of these examinations is that produced by Fleishman and Hempel (1956). The analysis of relative importance of several abilities is reproduced in Fig. 13. The task involved was a discrimination reaction time test and the percentage of variance accounted for by several factors is illustrated at different stages during the learning process. In this particular task, the role of proprioception, or proprioceptively related abilities, is not great at any stage during the learning process. However, there is evidence concerning the changes in the importance of this ability from several different sources.

The first general statement regarding this change came from Fitts (1951). He felt that it was necessary to investigate the relative importance of exteroceptive and proprioceptive cues in the course of learning and suggested that '. . . visual control is important while an individual is learning a new perceptual-motor task. As performance becomes habitual, however, it is likely that proprioceptive feedback or "feel" becomes the more important.' This hypothesis later became the object of significant experimentation. There is, however, a problem in the methodology employed in the investigation, namely how increasing proprioceptive control may be demonstrated. Three different kinds of solution may be offered.

The most frequent method used has been that derived by Fleishman and co-workers in which individual differences are first assessed in the relevant abilities. For example, measures can be made of proprioceptive sensitivity by

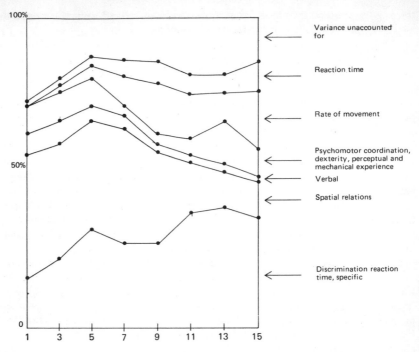

Fig. 13. Percentage of variance represented by each factor in a discrimination reaction time task. Percentage of variance is represented by the area of each factor. (Adapted from Fleishman and Hempel, Factorial analysis of complex psychomotor performance and related skills. Journal of Applied Psychology, 40, 96-104. Copyright 1956 American Psychological Association. Reprinted by permission.)

some psychophysical means and on this basis a group of subjects may be divided into those less sensitive and those more sensitive to this form of stimulation. Differences in performance during learning between these two groups should indicate differences in the importance of proprioception during the course of learning. A second method which may be used involves the presentation of a secondary or subsidiary task. For example, if visual cues become less important and proprioceptive cues more important, then two predictions may be made: (a) that a secondary task involving visual activity should have a progressively smaller disruptive effect on the major task as learning progresses, or (b) that a secondary task involving proprioception should have a progressively larger effect on the performance of the major task. A third method consists of anaesthetizing the relevant receptors at different stages during learning. According to the Fitts' hypothesis, disruption of proprioceptive feedback in this way should result in increasingly large decrements in performance as learning progresses.

The analysis of changing levels of proprioceptive importance has been made by Fleishman and Rich (1963). In their experiment a two hand coordination tracking task was used. Subjects were given two pretests. A measure of proprioceptive sensitivity was achieved by establishing difference thresholds for lifted weights using the method of limits (see Chapter Three). A measure of visual spatial ability was taken using a United States Air Force Aerial Orientation Test. In the subsequent experiment, subjects were required to keep a 'target follower' on a small target disc whilst the target moved in an irregular pattern at varying rates around a circular plate. The target follower was controlled by means of two independent, hand operated handles of the lathe type. It was found that the two pretests accounted in total for over fifty per cent of the variance in performance on the tracking task. The correlation of the two pretests with performance at different stages during learning, however, showed markedly contrasting patterns. Initially the correlation of the spatial ability test with performance was a significant 0.36. As learning proceeded this correlation decreased until on trial 10 the correlation was an insignificant 0.01. Converseley, the correlation of the proprioceptive measure was initially 0.03, but increased regularly over trials to reach a maximum of 0.40 on trial 10. Fleishman and Rich presented these data in a different form to make the point graphically. Figures 14 and 15 show the results they derived by dividing the total subject group into high and low sensitivity subsets on the two ability measures. At first those highly sensitive to spatial cues showed marked superiority over those less sensitive, whereas later in learning the difference between the subgroups disappeared. On the other hand, there was no difference initially between those more and less sensitive to proprioceptive information, but as learning progressed those in the more sensitive category produced increasingly better performances. In the first figure, there were significant differences between the two groups on the first trial and in the second figure, significant differences between the groups on the last trial.

These results are fine evidence for the Fitts hypothesis that proprioceptive cues are of the greatest relevance during later stages in learning. Fleishman and Rich considered that in the first few trials exteroceptive cues provide information for the guidance of movement indicated by the target course. It is these cues which assist the subjects in learning the spatial relationship between the proper control handle and handle movement. During this stage, proprioceptive cues are of little use to the subject since there has not been sufficient opportunity for the subject to learn which proprioceptive cues are associated with accurate performance, as errors tend to be large at this stage. Later in the course of learning or, 'once a given level of proficiency is reached and errors tend to be smaller, spatial cues are not as effective in facilitating more precise control over the target follower. The subjects high in spatial ability have an advantage only in earlier stages of learning. To achieve a higher

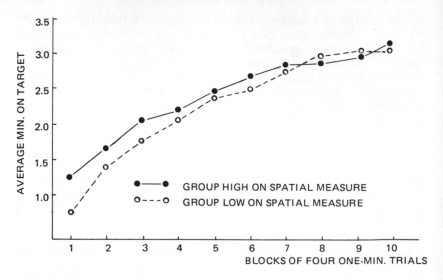

Fig. 14. Performance of groups high and low in sensitivity to spatial measures (Fleishman and Rich, J. Exp. Psychol. **66**, *6-11. Copyright 1963 by the American Psychological Association. Reprinted by permission.)*

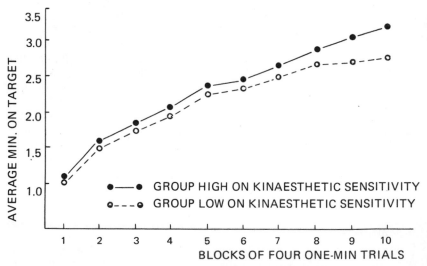

Fig. 15. Performance of groups high and low in sensitivity to proprioceptive measures (Fleishman and Rich, J. Exp. Psychol. **66**, *6-11. Copyright 1963 by the American Psychological Association. Reprinted by permission.)*

score, fine motor adjustments are required. Those subjects who are especially sensitive to proprioceptive cues are able to make use of this information earlier in the practice period. In a sense, they may be able to switch from a dependence on exteroceptive feedback to the more direct proprioceptive channels.' (Fleishman and Rich, 1963, pp. 11).

Other tests of the hypothesis have not been so unambiguous, and in fact some contradictory evidence has been found. In tests involving the gross motor skill of bowling, Phillips and Summers (1954) used a pretest of arm position sensitivity in order to measure the capacity of subjects to appreciate proprioceptive cues. Performance in the pretests was related to changes in the bowling score of the subjects categorised as either fast or slow learners. Phillips and Summers tentatively concluded that proprioceptive sensitivity was more important in the early part of the learning process. This result is diametrically opposed to that found by Fleishman and Rich (1963). The answer to the contradiction may be found partly in an assumption made by Phillips and Summers (1954). They assumed that those achieving low scores in the initial bowling test had the least experience of the skill and it was on this basis that their data were analysed. If this assumption was unwarranted, and no post-experimental check was reported, then the conclusion may not be appropriate.

Dickinson (1969) attempted to resolve the contradiction using a new experimental task. In this experiment, subjects were required to learn to serve a badminton shuttlecock into a target. Novice subjects were used, and their performance over one hundred trials was recorded. Performance was then correlated with the results of two pretests. One of these sampled accuracy of distance perception (exteroceptive sensitivity) and the other established sensitivity to lifted weights by the same method used by Fleishman and Rich (1963). The results of the experiment indicated that sensitivity to the distance cues did not correlate significantly with performance at any stage during learning, indicating that either exteroceptive cues are irrelevant to this type of task, or more likely, sensitivity to the wrong kind of exteroceptive cues was sampled. The results of correlations between proprioceptive sensitivity and aiming were more interesting. These are given in *Table 1*.

Table 1 Correlation of proprioceptive sensitivity and aiming score

Sets of 20 trials	Correlation of proprioceptive sensitivity and aiming	p.
1	0.39	0.03
2	0.50	0.005
3	0.40	0.02
4	0.52	0.005
5	0.48	0.007

Following Fleishman and Rich (1963), the results were also presented graphically by dividing the total group at the median into those less and more sensitive to proprioceptive cues and the performances of these two groups over trials were recorded. The results of this analysis are shown in Fig. 16. There was a significant difference between the groups at each stage during learning. Both the correlations and the analysis by group appear to show, therefore, that a consistent and highly important role can be assigned to proprioceptive sensitivity throughout the learning process. This result contradicts both the findings of Fleishman and Rich (1963) and the conclusion of Phillips and Summers (1954). The discrepancy cannot be explained easily if the original Fitts hypothesis is correct. However, it is possible that differences between tasks in terms of their response requirements may be used as an explanation. 'In Fleishman's test of two-hand coordination, it was necessary for the subject to respond constantly to exteroceptive cues. In this badminton aiming task, exteroceptive cues were only an intermittent source of feedback, to which response was made without any reference to externally dictated patterns of receptor/effector activity.

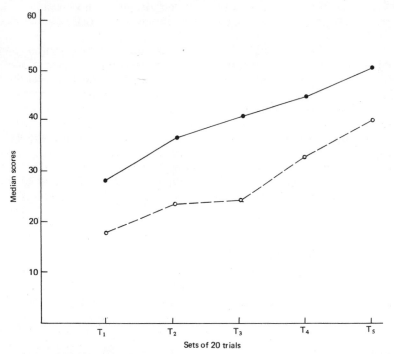

Fig. 16. Performance of groups high (●—●) and low (○- - -○) in sensitivity to proprioceptive measures (Dickinson, 1969).

This may explain to some degree the insignificant relation between distance perception and aiming scores. Similarly, as learning progresses in a tracking skill, changing patterns of cue redundancy may be based on differing perceptual emphases, whereas in aiming the perceptual demands may remain constant throughout the learning process.' (Dickinson, 1969, pp. 469). The argument advanced in this case, therefore, suggests that the Fitts hypothesis is not generally applicable to a large range of skills. However, more recent evidence has suggested that the Fleishman and Rich (1963) and the Dickinson (1969) results can be reconciled in a way which provides support for the Fitts hypothesis. In 1970 Dickinson replicated the aiming study using children between 10 and 11 years of age. Sensitivity to proprioceptive cues was again measured by means of the lifted weights technique. The reliability of this measure, incidentally, was found to be 0.76, which was somewhat lower than that reported by Fleishman and Rich (1963), perhaps not surprisingly. The results of this study showed again a correlation between the weight sensitivity and performance of the order shown in *Table 2*. The development of a

Table 2 Correlation of proprioceptive sensitivity and aiming score with children

Sets of 40 trials	Correlation or proprioceptive sensitivity and aiming	p.
1	0.17	N.S.
2	0.31	0.05
3	0.36	0.01
4	0.38	0.01
5	0.35	0.01

relationship shows a trend in the direction predicted by the Fitts hypothesis. Further analysis of the results, however, revealed less straightforward support. Subjects were divided on the basis of whether they had ever participated in a racket game or handled a racket. The subjects had completed an information sheet prior to the experiment. The results showed a significant difference in the correlations as shown in *Table 3*. It is apparent that experienced children

Table 3 Correlation between aiming and proprioceptive sensitivity for groups with different levels of experience

Sets of 40 Trials	Aiming/Proprioceptive Sensitivity for Experienced Group	Aiming/Proprioceptive sensitivity for Novice Group
1	0.63	0.12
2	0.61	0.02
3	0.67	0.06
4	0.79	0.15
5	0.67	0.01

showed the same pattern of correlation as the novice adults, that is, a high, significant and consistent relationship between aiming performance and proprioceptive sensitivity. The novice children showed no such relationship and did not give any indication of the development of a correlation over a large number of trials. The inference to be drawn from this result may be expressed in the following terms. Experience on the part of the children raised their level of performance beyond the stage at which proprioceptive cues become important. Presumably the adult novices in the first experiment had had sufficient experience in non-badminton aiming tasks for them to transfer elements of the skill to the new situation and hence achieved a level at which proprioceptive cues were almost immediately the most relevant. It is possible that the length of the learning period for the novice children was insufficient for the development of this relationship. 'The evidence appears to suggest that kinaesthetic sensitivity is not an important ability when the [child] has no experience. On the other hand, children with some experience of badminton tend to produce results which are similar to those found with adults who had no experience.' (Dickinson, 1970). This difference between adults and children may be explained in terms of transfer. A more appealing explanation can be suggested stemming from Fleishman's ability concept. It will be remembered from Chapter Four that Fleishman suggested that abilities may develop during childhood and thereafter remain relatively constant. If it is assumed that aiming is such an ability and one which has a high component of proprioceptive sensitivity, it may be inferred that the experienced children and the adult novices showed this ability whereas the inexperienced children had not had sufficient experience for the ability to develop.

A novel method of testing for increasing value of proprioceptive feedback was used by West (1967). He investigated the capacity of typists at different stages in the acquisition process in performance without vision. In essence this represents a cross-sectional rather than longitudinal study of changes in dependence upon vision. The results indicated greater dependence on vision for those subjects in the early stages of acquisition and higher levels of dependence on proprioceptive feedback for accomplished typists.

The second method of detecting increasing importance for proprioception was described earlier as relying on the use of a secondary task. It appears that very little research has used this method to date. Without specifying the role of proprioception, however, Bahrick, Noble and Fitts (1954) presented some indirect evidence. The major task involved subjects pressing response keys in response to a changing stimulus display in which there was some preview of the visual display. In addition to this task subjects were required to solve arithmetical problems mentally. The results indicated that as learning of the task progressed beyond a given point, no further improvements in the major task were produced but continued learning was detectable because of increased capacity to perform the secondary task. Although at the time Bahrick et al did not examine this result from the point of view of proprioception's increasing importance, being more interested in this technique for indicating long term learning, at a later date Fitts (1964) re-examined the results and suggested that they supported the contention that proprioceptive control becomes increasingly important. As subjects delegated control to proprioception, they were thereby able to release greater attention to solving the arithmetic problems. It must be noted that in this experiment, the influence on the secondary task only held good for the situation in which the major responses were repetitive and in fact, highly predictable. A similar point was made by Welford (1968). 'Where conditions require or permit virtually exact repetition of a unit many times, performance tends to become stereotyped in the course of practice, and the whole cycle can be run off very much as a chain response with each member acting as the cue for the one that follows.' The prediction therefore is made that proprioceptive stimuli become the cues for subsequent activities, but it is required that the skill be regular and predictable. This distinction between predictable and unpredictable, or regular against flexible skills, reveals a potential area of exception to the Fitts hypothesis. Presumably the increasing importance of proprioception can only occur in those tasks which may be conducted using a pattern of movement which occurs regularly. Where a skill depends largely on flexibility of response to many different kinds of exteroceptive cues, it would seem unlikely that proprioceptive control could ever achieve a high level of significance. Knapp (1963) distinguished between athletic skills of a mainly 'habit' variety and those with a dominant reliance on perceptual aspects. She suggested that one way of classifying skills was to place them upon a continuum between the extremes of habit and perceptual orientation. Essentially this view is a refinement of Poulton's (1957) dichotomy between open and closed skills. It is logical to assume that Fitts' hypothesis is most readily applied only to those skills which fall at the habit end of the continuum. In terms of athletic skills for example, discus throwing or high board diving may have as their goal an habitual reproduction of physical movements and therefore there may be an increasing delegation of control of proprioceptive feedback. On the other hand, skills such as football or tennis are by their very nature flexible and the development of habits may even prove detrimental to the level of performance. In these skills the exteroceptive cues are likely to maintain their high levels of importance throughout the learning process. It is possible that within these non-habit skills there are sub-routines which may become habitual and in which visual factors may decrease in performance. For example, the results of Dickinson's (1969, 1970a) studies appear to support the view that proprioceptive cues may be highly important in the serve after learning has occurred (whether as a result of transfer or specific training) and yet the game of badminton in total may be assessed as depending significantly on responsiveness to exteroceptive cues even at the highest level of skill.

Two further kinds of method remain to be discussed in the analysis of increasing proprioceptive control. The technique of providing a secondary task which produces proprioceptive stimulation, which should become increasingly disruptive as learning progresses, has not been the object of research as far as the author is aware. The design of experiments using proprioceptive interference may involve some difficulties particularly in providing two tasks which do not mechanically interfere with each other. Progress towards such a design has been made in the author's laboratory to test not only the hypothesis that proprioception increases in relative importance but also to test an additonal hypothesis generated from the evidence discussed next.

This evidence has been produced from the use of the final method of investigation, the anaesthetizing of proprioceptors at different stages of learning. This evidence was reviewed in Chapter Four where it was noted that studies involving the disruption of proprioceptive feedback in this way do not, in many cases, cause significant decrements in performance. In fact these results are superficially highly negative evidence for the Fitts hypothesis since the tasks involved were both relatively common every-day movements which could be assumed to have been well learned by the subjects and were also highly repetitive and regular in nature (see Laszlo, 1967, 1968). If the Fitts hypothesis were accurate one should predict that the better learned the task, the greater would be the decrement in performance following the blocking of proprioceptive feedback.

A possible reconciliation between the evidence supporting the Fitts hypothesis and that supporting the motor programming view was made by Laszlo and Bairstow (1971). Their experiment was described in Chapter Four. Briefly stated, Laszlo and Bairstow provided data suggesting that the control of rate of movement is possible in the absence of proprioceptive feedback, but improvement in the accuracy of movement is not possible where proprioceptive information is disrupted. In other words, those overlearned tasks which showed little impairment in performance when proprioceptive cues were disrupted were mainly tasks in which the measure of competence in performance was established by assessing rate.

An alternative hypothesis is possible which would involve extending the Fitts hypothesis to the case of overlearning. That is, proprioceptive information is of relatively minor importance at first. Gradually the relevance of proprioceptive cues increases until some maximum level is achieved. From this point onwards as proprioceptive feedback gives repeated positive reinforcement—or informs the organism that the task has been completed successfully, the accurate motor response becomes habitual. The result of this high level of motor response accuracy is that proprioceptive stimuli become increasingly redundant. After considerable overlearning, the disruption of proprioceptive information will no longer cause any significant decrement in performance.

This point may be amplified on the basis of the Fitts and Posner (1967) analysis of stages of learning. They suggested that three phases may be identified in the learning of repetitive or habitual tasks. In the first, or cognitive, stage the learner discovei..j the objectives of the task and identifies responses and stimuli which are relevant for its completion. In the second stage or associative phase, the relevant stimuli and responses are matched and although errors still occur, the learner is aware of the mistakes made and the reasons for them. During this phase the errors are gradually eliminated. It is not until the final autonomous phase that the skill becomes, in a sense, automatic. 'During the final phase of skill learning, component processes become increasingly autonomous, less directly subject to cognitive control, and less subject to interference from other ongoing activities or environmental distractions.' (Fitts and Posner, 1967, pp. 14). It is reasonable to assume that in the first stage visual control is of paramount importance. During the second stage the visual input becomes of relatively less value and proprioceptive information increases in relative importance. In the final stage, Fitts and Posner would probably argue that proprioception is the major controlling agent. However, it is contended here that further changes occur as the autonomous phase continues, resulting in the gradual decrease of proprioceptive control and the development of a motor programming system. There is evidence already available that repetitive tasks show improvement over many years of practice (Crossman, 1959). In other words, there are known changes in performance during the autonomous phase. The change from proprioceptive to motor programming control may be one of those changes.

In order to test the hypothesis experiments could be designed which involve the use of a major skill task and an intermittent subsidiary task which would provide interfering proprioceptive information. The task may consist of a repetitive series of finger movements of one hand whereas the secondary task could be large scale movements of the other arm. The hypothesis would be that there would be a gradually increasing decrement in the performance of the initial task (as proprioceptive cues become more important). After overlearning smaller and smaller decrements should result as the major skill becomes increasingly the result of motor programming.

It is equally likely that these results would also be predicted if anaesthetizing proprioceptors were to occur intermittently during the learning and over-learning of a novel skill. That is, in the initial stages of the learning process only relatively minor decrements in performance would result. As the task was learned and proprioceptive control increased, disruption of this form of feedback would result in large decrements in performance, but after overlearning the result might be the reduction of decrement due to anaesthetizing. This latter prediction conforms to the evidence found by previous experimenters with this technique who used highly overlearned movements.

Methodologically, one point needs to be emphasized. The use of the anaesthetic or the secondary task needs to be restricted to infrequent sampling periods. In other words, the skill must develop 'normally'. If continuous or frequent test trials are given it is possible that different strategies of control would be developed by subjects in order to compensate for the disruptive influences. It remains for the research to be completed before further discussion of the value of this hypothesis can be made.

Although the changing importance of proprioception during learning has been discussed at some length, little consideration has been given so far to the reasons for this change. In the previous sections, occasional reference was made to the 'delegation' of control to proprioception. This provides the clue to the function of increasing proprioceptive importance. Such delegation enables the learner's visual attention to be directed elsewhere. That is, proprioceptive monitoring releases the visual system for sampling other aspects of the environment. Gibbs (1970) referred to the process in this way: 'It is hypothesized that exteroceptive feedback is dominant in the early learning of all tasks and skills. A main function of learning is to permit the use of lower loops in the hierarchy by delegating detailed duties of monitoring from exteroceptors to proprioceptors. A major function of such delegation is to reduce demands on visual attention. The relations between the output and proprioceptive feedback must be learned to permit delegation of monitoring. The duration of delegation depends on the predictability of the effects of a given activity upon the environment.' (Gibbs, 1970, pp. 222).

A large proportion of proprioceptive information, it will be remembered, does not directly reach the cortex. The processing of this information occurs at lower centres, particularly the cerebellum, and hence total attentional capacity is likely to gain considerably from increases in proprioceptive control. The same argument may, of course, be used in relation to the hypothetical delegation of proprioceptive control to motor programming. In this context it should be remembered that proprioceptive stimuli arising from the joint receptors do have direct connections with the cortex and therefore employ attentional capacity. It is reasonable to assume that should motor programming result from high levels of learning, it is probable that the function of the process is the release of attention to an even greater extent. Although speculative this is a logical corollary to the motor programming hypothesis. The concept of attention has so far been used without any attempt at either definition or discussion. The next section is concerned with this aspect of behaviour and the relevance of attention to proprioceptive cues in the learning process.

Attention to Proprioceptive Information

In Guthrie's (1959) exposition of the learning process, he stressed the role of the attention organisms pay to the stimuli derived both from internal and external sources. It has only been relatively recently that the concept of attention has once again attained respectability in psychological circles. The early behaviourists considered attention one of many mentalistic concepts for which there was no room in the objective study of behaviour. The traditional stimulus-response theorist seldom referred to the idea of attention and it is quite surprising to find Guthrie resuscitating the concept in his theory—even though he did not fully or satisfactorily define the term. And as Mackworth (1970) noted: '(Attention) . . . is as basic to the human psychological experiment as gravity is to the universe . . . Psychological studies on the human nearly always begin with directing the subject's attention towards the material that is the basis of the experiment, asking the subject to learn this, discriminate that, or rank order those stimuli, and so on. In most experiments the nature of the task is such that the subject finds it interesting, and has no difficulty in maintaining the necessary attention. Consequently, failures in attention need not be taken into account.' (Mackworth, 1970, pp. 13). Mackworth went on to explain that this is not the case in tests of vigilance. In the context of learning processes the concept of the subject's attention may be of critical importance. In any task, cues or stimuli, both exteroceptive and proprioceptive, must be attended to in order for the organism to perform accurately. It is beyond the scope of this work to detail current theories of attention. Suffice to say that whilst qualitative judgments concerning attention have long been possible, it is only with the advent of the concept of capacity taken from information theory, that quantitative measures of attention have become possible (see for example, Broadbent, 1958). Unfortunately, the quantitative assessment of attention cannot be applied in the case of proprioception since the stimuli are internally produced and may not be manipulated by the experimenter in the same way as visual stimuli. Also, subjects are capable of giving verbal reports identifying visual and auditory stimuli. There is no such language to describe the proprioceptive stimuli. Finally, there is the problem that only a proportion, perhaps a minority, of proprioceptive stimuli reach the cortex directly and to which attention may be directed. However, since some receptors do connect directly with the cortex it is possible to make qualitative statements, though they be speculative, on the nature of attention to proprioceptive stimuli in the learning process.

During the early sessions of learning a skill, (the cognitive phase as Fitts and Posner (1967) described it) the learner begins to identify which cues or stimuli are important for performance. Since the whole of the stimulus array, both proprioceptive and exteroceptive cannot be attended to, the learner gradually acquires the ability to attend selectively to only the relevant stimuli. This process of identification of relevant stimuli, in whatever modality, reduces the load on the learner by requiring him to attend to fewer stimuli. It has become an objective in the investigation of specific skills to identify exactly what these stimuli are in order that teaching may be more effective. If a relevant stimulus can be identified and the learner's attention directed towards it, the learner will be relieved of the process of trial-and-error seeking for appropriate stimuli. This problem is hindered in terms of proprioception since the stimuli cannot be verbalized precisely. There is a further problem which was first pointed out by Miller, Galanter and Pribram (1960). They noted that in many skills the learner must identify and attend to stimuli which are relevant for himself. They contended that the stimuli, which provide adequate cues for one person may be different for another, that relevant stimuli may in fact be idiosyncratic. Welford (1968), however, noted that '... practice seems to enable the skilled performer to select from among the mass of data impinging on his sense organs so that he neglects much of what is, to an unskilled person, striking, and reacts strongly to data that a normal observer would fail to notice'.

Whether the cues are universal or idiosyncratic will obviously depend upon the type of skill and the problem will be more adequately discussed in the chapter on training. It is still relevant, however, to mention that subjects must learn to attend and respond to both proprioceptive and exteroceptive stimuli which may arrive simultaneously. Two separate issues therefore become important. Firstly, can man attend to and process stimuli which involve more than one modality and secondly, is it possible for the learner to process signals which are simultaneous? These problems are not easily investigated in terms of proprioception because of the experimental difficulties previously mentioned. There is evidence on both of these aspects from other modalities.

In the case of signals or stimuli arising in different modalities there are some interesting data which suggest that in many circumstances stimuli arising in two modalities are processed successively, even where they occur simultaneously. The doctrine of prior entry has been investigated fairly thoroughly (see Boring, 1942) and the research indicates two things. Firstly, that man is limited in his capacity to attend to stimuli from more than one source and secondly, that some assessment is made on the part of the observer as to the relative importance of the simultaneous signals. The signal accorded the higher level of priority is attended to and processed first. It has already been shown (Rock and Harris, 1967; Legge, 1965) that man tends to give high priority to visual signals. It is possible that proprioceptive stimuli must be delayed in terms of processing time. In continuous tasks a delay in processing stimuli is, of course, likely to make that signal of relatively little value. Perhaps this accounts for the fact that studies such as that by Fleishman and Rich (1963) showed no difference between those with high proprioceptive sensitivity and those with low, in the initial stages of learning.

Fitts and Posner (1967) pointed out that: 'Man can process signals simultaneously if they are highly regular or predictable'. As signals become redundant a subject may find it possible to react as quickly to two signals together as to either alone. The author has noted previously (Dickinson, 1972) that it is axiomatic that with increasing skill the learner is likely to find tasks increasingly predictable. As the level of experience increases in a particular task, therefore, the capacity to respond to simultaneous feedback from different sources may also increase. For example, specific exteroceptive and proprioceptive cues may occur simultaneously at some point in a particular task. During the cognitive phase it is probable that exteroceptive cues are attended to first since given a higher priority by the subject. Processing of the proprioceptive cues may either be delayed or not occur at all. Later in the learning process, since these stimuli always occur simultaneously, both may be processed or at least attention to visual cues may be released so that processing of proprioceptive information occurs. As the learner finds out more about the skill, therefore, he is not only capable of attending to more relevant cues but may also be able to attend to more cues in total.

Researchers into the phenomenon of attention in Russia (e.g. Sokolov, 1960) have tended to equate attention with the orientation reaction. Zaporozhets (1961) maintained that in any skill learning situation the learner must make a series of orientiation reactions to each new stimulus complex as it occurs during the skill. The orientation reaction, sometimes called the 'what-is-it?' reaction, is best regarded in this context as an attending response. Zaporozhets reported that directing young children's attention to their hand movements enabled them to learn a skill much more easily than other children, who, Zaporozhets claimed, are more usually interested in the end result of their action instead of the means by which it is achieved. Lynn (1966) has pointed out that equating the orientation reaction, which is defined mainly in terms of physiological responses, with attention may not be entirely acceptable; attending responses are to a much greater extent learned. As Lynn put it: 'In reducing the problem of selective attention to the problem of orientation reactions in this manner it is possible that Zaporozhets has pointed the way to an advance in our understanding of the nature of attention; or, he may be begging quite a big question. Whether orientation reactions are an invariable concomitant of attention is a question that deserves further research.' (Lynn, 1966, pp. 86). Alluisi (1966) quoted evidence that performance changes in attention tasks have been found in the absence of physiological change in the organism, which seems to provide support for Lynn's criticism.

Proprioceptive Pattern Recognition

Pattern recognition is an area of research which is related to that of attention. The two fields overlap considerably. Until this point, discussion has revolved around the identification of proprioceptive stimuli or cues as though these cues were single feedback entities. Obviously this is an over-simplification. These stimuli consist of many simultaneous inputs from proprioceptors. Essentially when we discuss the learner correctly identifying a proprioceptive cue, it is more accurate to say that he has learned to recognize a pattern of proprioceptive stimulation. Again, however, the evidence for proprioceptive pattern recognition is limited since patterns cannot be examined or manipulated objectively and discussion must be based primarily on evidence from other modalities.

Smith (1969) speculated on the way in which patterns of proprioceptive stimulation may be used in movement control. According to her analysis the characteristics of movement receptors are that: receptors adapt rapidly to static positioning of the limbs and that many of these receptors respond to only one direction of movement and most show changes in the frequency of discharge dependent upon velocity, but that velocity thresholds differ for different groups of receptors. She went on: 'With the feedback available from the position and movement receptors, complex patterns can be established and perhaps "coded" in the sensorimotor cortex.' This coding system, Smith maintained, could depend on responses from a single receptor and from a multireceptor complex. Although Smith (1969) related these patterns to performance she did not offer any suggestions concerning the role of proprioceptive pattern recognition in learning. Yet it would be difficult to imagine that pattern recognition of this sort is innate. Dodwell (1970) contended that 'higher order' variables, by which he referred to attention, motivation and learning or experience, are certain to influence pattern recognition. In fact the effect of prior learning on this phenomenon is a source of experimental difficulty for researchers into visual pattern recognition since it is almost impossible to provide pattern recognition tasks which are entirely novel and free from transfer effects. Where the problem has been solved by using nonsense patterns, it has been shown that learning to correctly identify patterns is a somewhat lengthy process, particularly where there are changes (distortions) in the pattern (Fitts and Posner, 1967). This is of course the situation in a real-life skill, where each repetition is likely to be at least slightly different causing changes in proprioceptive input.

It is possible to take two distinct points of view regarding the influence of proprioceptive pattern recognition. Firstly, we may agree with Smith (1969) and suggest that pattern recognition is essential for movement control. That is, that man must recognize proprioceptive patterns in order to appreciate movement. Secondly, it may be argued that pattern recognition is a function of increasing level of skill, low levels of performance being possible in the absence of pattern recognition, but as skill level increases, patterns of proprioceptive stimuli come to be recognized and responses made to them. Probably both points are correct. Patterns of proprioceptive stimulation are probably learned from childhood and an enormous capacity to recognize patterns is developed. However, in learning an entirely new skill, only a proportion of this previous learning may transfer to the new situation and a new set of patterns may have to be learned. The point has been made repeatedly that skill learning is highly specific. Perhaps part of this specificity derives from the learning of unique patterns of proprioceptive stimulation for individual skills.

There is evidence from developmental research into visual perception that pattern recognition, in very simple form, occurs in young infants (e.g. Lang, 1965; Spears, 1964), but that as visual patterns become more complex prior experience is essential. Dodwell (1970) postulated that there is a built-in primary detector system which is present at birth and it is this system which enables infant pattern-recognition and also forms the basis upon which the later development of pattern perception is built. Perhaps the same is also true for the recognition of proprioceptive patterns in the infant.

Fitts and Posner (1967) noted that the recognition of a pattern is highly efficient in terms of information processing since it allows the organism to respond to what are really several stimuli, simultaneously presented. However, they pointed out that pattern recognition may not be an unmitigated advantage. As a pattern becomes more easily recognized, its identification is less disrupted by distortion. That is, the pattern may be recognized despite some changes in the component stimulus parts. This may be an advantage in some situations but this is not inevitable. Fitts and Posner (1967) used the following example. 'Knowing the content of a radio or T.V. programme can help you follow it despite distortion. On the other hand, in proof-reading we may fail to detect an error (distortion) because the context leads us to expect and thus, in spite of the distortion, to see the correct pattern.' Perhaps this is one reason why conflicting information derived in two sense modalities (see Chapter Four) may not be reported as such. That is, stimulus patterns arising from proprioceptive sources which conflict with visual patterns may be 'felt' as providing the 'correct' feedback pattern in spite of the fact that the stimulation in reality is very different.

Patterns of visual stimulation have generally been examined in terms of spatial presentations. A pattern of stimulation may also have a temporal variable. The understanding of words is an example of pattern recognition in which component stimuli are received over time. Proprioceptive patterns of stimulation may also be thought of as occuring over time particularly in tasks which are continuous. One function of learning may therefore be the earlier identification of a particular pattern because of recognition of the first component elements. This is certainly the case in other modalities. For example, the ends of words are much more redundant than the beginning of words, and understanding of words is simply an overlearned auditory pattern recognition task. The influence of sequential redundancy through learning has been previously explained many times in terms of responding to exteroceptive cues (see Knapp, 1963). As the learner acquires the capacity to identify a pattern through its earliest component stimuli his response can be made faster within the skill situation. Instead of waiting for the sequential pattern to be completed, responding may occur prior to the completion. There may be an equivalent process in terms of proprioceptive patterns of stimulation. As the learner increases his knowledge of patterns of proprioceptive feedback occurring over time, it may be possible for response to be initiated at earlier points thereby increasing apparent reaction speed. Consider, for example, the proprioceptive stimulation induced passively in a judo exponent by his opponent, or by the machine in a pilot, ignoring for the moment exteroceptive patterns. In both cases proprioceptive stimulation occurs and responses are necessary. Presumably experience or learning enables the learner to identify the onset of a particular pattern and make rapid adequate adjustment, whereas the novice may not recognize the pattern hence be later—perhaps too late—in initiating a response.

Proprioceptive Sensitivity and Learning

In Chapter Three the techniques of measuring proprioceptive sensitivity were discussed. It was pointed out that in a large number of instances thresholds, both absolute and differential, had been established for proprioception. The question discussed here is whether these thresholds change as a function of learning. Does the highly skilled individual respond to more relevant cues more accurately, or is he also more sensitive to any proprioceptive stimuli? There is some evidence that this is the case. From a purely experimental point of view, psychophysical technqiues generally recommend a warm-up period in which the subject becomes accustomed to the task and in which performance stabilises. This warm-up period is very often a period of improvement in sensitivity. However, this change is not usually considered as learning. More pertinent to the discussion is the evidence produced by Robinson (1969) who showed that there was a consistent improvement over trials in the proprioceptive psychophysical judgments of children. Whilst this may be construed as a result of increasing familiarity of the subjects with the test and what was required of them, the change in performance is consistent with any definition of learning, and Robinson refers to the improvement as a learning curve. There is also indirect evidence available from Phillips and Summers (1954) on this point. They found that proprioceptive sensitivity was greater in the dominant arm rather than the non-dominant. This could indicate that the increased experience of movement and proprioceptive feedback from the dominant arm had caused a reduction in the thresholds to proprioceptive stimuli compared with the non-dominant. Similarly, the evidence discussed in Chapter Three from Lloyd and Caldwell (1965) in their investigation into active and passive proprioceptive sensitivity of the leg, is indicative of a learning influence. They found position sensitivity to be greatest within that arc of the leg used in normal gait. The interpretation could again be that increased sensitivity was a result of overlearning in that movement.

An explanation of these results may also be advanced in terms of signal detection theory. Assuming that proprioceptive signals arise against a background of proprioceptive 'noise', it is possible that the reinforcement provided to the learner over trials, (the fact that he is correct, rewarded or given praise for example) enables him to optimise the placement of cut-off points. In other words, knowledge of results or reinforcement may indicate to the subject stimuli associated with accurate decisions which both minimize misses and false positives. Whether explanations are given in terms of optimised cut-off points or in terms of reduced thresholds, the net result is the same; an apparent increase in sensitivity within those movements which are familiar.

The skilled performer is therefore in a distinctly advantageous position compared with the novice. He has identified and attends to the relevant rather than irrelevant stimuli, increased his efficiency of responding by identifying spatial and temporal patterns of stimuli and, since he has become familiar with the task, may also have increased sensivitiy to proprioceptive stimuli.

Proprioception and Transfer of Training

In learning any new skill, the learner brings with him to the new situation a vast experience of skill learning. No new skill is ever learned entirely without drawing on past experience by the adult. Even the most novel of laboratory tasks take for granted that there will be some transfer from previous experience. Transfer of training in the laboratory is usually defined as 'the effect that the practice of one task has upon the learning or performance of a second'. (Cratty, 1967). This may be extended in terms of real life situations by emphasising that the learning of many different previous tasks may influence the learning of a new task.

A phenomenon of such centrality to behaviour has obviously attracted a great deal of research and theoretical argument from the behavioural scientists. Evidence has been gathered in verbal rote learning as well as skill learning, in concept learning and in problem solving. In the area of skill learning Cratty (1967) has listed the following 11 principles of transfer. (Other reviews of transfer in skill learning may be found in Knapp, 1963, and Holding, 1965, and more technically in Battig, 1966.)

1 Transfer is greatest when the training conditions of two tasks are highly similar.

2 When the task requires the same response to a new but similar stimulus, positive transfer increases as the stimulus conditions become more alike.

3 When the task requires the learner to make a new or different response to the same stimuli, transfer tends to be negative and increases as the responses become less similar.

4 If the responses in the transfer task are different from those in the original task, then the more similar the stimuli, the less the positive transfer.

5 Continued practice in learning a number of related tasks leads to increased facility in learning how to learn.

6 Transfer is greatest if greater effort is extended during the early part of a series of related tasks.

7 Insight occurs with more frequency as extensive practice is gained in a series of related tasks.

8 Transfer can occur as the result of 'cognitive links' formed between two tasks.

9 The greater the amount of practice on the original task, the greater the transfer.

10 Time elapsing between the original and transfer tasks is not critical unless specific details must be remembered.

11 Transfer is greater if the performer understands general principles which are appropriate to two or more tasks (Cratty, 1967, pp. 297).

Although these statements are generalizations which might not go entirely unchallenged, they represent a large proportion of the evidence for transfer in motor skill learning.

The relationship of proprioception to the transfer of skills has not been investigated with the same thoroughness accorded other aspects. However, certain elements of this relationship have been established. It is possible first of all to contend that the ability/skill distinction dealt with earlier in this chapter may also be viewed as being a transfer phenomenon. Fleishman (1966) has noted that underlying abilities may be the product of learning or genetic factors. Those abilities which depend on learning may be conceived as contributing to the performance of any new task which is encountered and demands those abilities. The learner shows a higher level of performance or rate of learning as a function of previous experience which has developed these abilities. Since many of Fleishman's ability traits encompass proprioception in its many forms (see Chapter Four), and since it has also been established that learning may influence proprioceptive sensitivity, it is not unreasonable to assume that positive transfer in new skill situations may be attributable in some measure to the influence of proprioception.

There are two significant differences between transfer in this context and transfer of training as usually explored in the laboratory. In the laboratory, transfer is generally examined with reference to two tasks presented sequentially or at least with a relatively short time interval between. In considering the influence of abilities such as proprioceptive sensitivity as transfer, the time scale may be vastly different. Fleishman (1966) noted that an ability is usually developed in childhood whereas the novel task to which that previous learning transfers may take place during adulthood. Similarly, the ability may be developed on the basis of a large range of tasks, whereas in the laboratory a single task is usually employed for the original learning. It is clear, however, that transfer of training and the ability/skill paradigm have much in common and may differ only quantitatively rather than qualitatively.

In the study of transfer in the laboratory, Gibbs (1970) has credited proprioception with a salient role. He rejected available theories of transfer of training in skill, describing these theories as inadequate. Instead Gibbs established a servo-control system model and observed that similarities exist between the action of the model and transfer effects. The model has already been described in Chapter Four.

It was Gibbs' contention that there is a hierarchy of control loops in the central nervous system, for example visual control loops and proprioceptive control loops. As learning progresses there may be changes in the relative importance of a control loop. (A restatement of the Fitts (1951) hypothesis). The amount of transfer of skill or the type of transfer that will occur in a given situation is dependent upon the control loop in operation. Tasks which demand visual monitoring and are similar in respect of response characteristics show large amounts of positive transfer, since the same control loop is effective in both situations, despite other marked differences between the tasks. Gibbs quoted the following illustration from an experiment in continuous tracking. 'In one study (Gibbs 1954) there was about 90 per cent of positive transfer in both directions between a conventional free-moving control lever and a pressure-operated lever, although the effects of a given deflection of the two levers differed in the ratio of 40 to 1.' (Gibbs 1970, pp. 222).

In step-input tracking, the learning process involves the delegation of monitoring to proprioceptive feedback loops. It would be predicted therefore that positive transfer should occur between step-input tracking tasks which vary in other dimensions but have the property of proprioceptive monitoring in common. However, within the category of proprioceptive control there may be entirely different feedback sub-systems operating which would invalidate this prediction. Thus, if the same two control levers are used as described in the continuous tracking experiment (one free-moving and the other pressure operated) for step-input tracking, the proprioceptive feedback experienced during learning would be entirely different in the two tasks. In one case proprioceptive information would be available from isotonic muscular contraction as well as joint movement; in the case of the pressure operated lever isometric muscular contraction would produce proprioceptive feedback and very little movement would occur. Therefore the proprioceptive feedback would be entirely different and a more compelling prediction would be that in this situation there would be no transfer between the two levers. Gibbs (1965) found support for this hypothesis when investigating transfer in both directions. No positive, and in one case high levels of negative, transfer were noted.

Gibbs (1970) generalized the findings and suggested that where two tasks with some degree of similarity are both influenced by visual control loops it is likely that positive transfer will occur. Alternatively, if two such tasks are monitored on the basis of proprioceptive feedback and the nature of the proprioceptive feedback is different, then either negative or no transfer will occur. In extending this argument to transfer pheonomena outside the laboratory, Gibbs (1970) was less clear in enunciating the reasons for some transfer effects involving proprioceptive control. Writing, Gibbs maintained, was a good example of a skill mainly under proprioceptive control. Yet there is high positive transfer to writing with whole arm movements as on a blackboard when the skill is usually performed with wrist and fingers and low levels of transfer to writing with the non-dominant hand. In both cases, the proprioceptive stimulation arising from the new task is very different from that in the original learning. The only explanation offered by Gibbs for these pheonomena is that: 'Groups of proprioceptors in specific muscles and joints that signal a right to left movement of one arm are activated by the opposite direction of movement of the other arm'. (Gibbs, 1970, pp. 224). He presented no evidence for this assumption and in any case it does little to resolve the problem of predicting the amount of transfer dependent on the type of proprioceptive control in use for the two tasks.

In discussing the relationship between habitual and novel incompatible skills the position taken by Gibbs (1970) has many similarities with the view expressed concerning Fleishman's ability/skill paradigm. Gibbs maintained that everyday movements serve to establish expected relationships between movement, on the one hand, and proprioceptive and exteroceptive feedback on the other. Where these relationships are disrupted in artificial laboratory tasks, negative transfer is likely to occur. In mirror tracing, for example, the habitual relationship between visual and proprioceptive feedback and movement is distorted and little positive transfer occurs to the new situation. Whereas Fleishman is mainly concerned with habitual relationships (abilities) giving positive transfer to novel skills, Gibbs explained that the transfer may be negative if the new task involves the incompatible (unusual) relationships between learned relationships and the new task.

The degree to which Gibbs' view of transfer with respect to a proprioceptive and exteroceptive control hierarchy is adequate to explain other phenomena remains to be seen. At the present it is, as Gibbs saw, speculative, but justified by the necessity to develop some systematic and experimental approach to transfer of skill which is not wholly dependent on the use of paradigms developed in the verbal learning context.

Proprioception and Retention

It is only recently that certain fundamental assumptions concerning memory in motor skill tasks have been seriously questioned. In the past the assumption has been made that forgetting occurs very quickly in verbal learning tasks, whereas retention levels have been thought to be high for motor skills. In fact many studies have failed to find forgetting at all in motor tasks. Bilodeau (1966) noted that the apparent absence of forgetting in experimental tasks made it impossible to determine the variables that produced forgetting when it occurred in real life situations. One of the reasons for this failure has been the way in which skilled performance has been measured. High levels of retention may be attributable to measurement artifacts rather than to the superiority of motor over verbal recall. For example, Bilodeau (1966) quoted the results of a simple lever positioning experiment in which no differences were found in mean training and recall scores. However, one measure of forgetting is the consistency of responding and when this aspect was examined, substantial differences between training and recall were established which would not necessarily be evident from mean values.

Another factor in the difficulty of exploring memory for motor tasks has been the fact that skill learning has often involved complex tasks in which perhaps a large proportion of the task has been overlearned, with a consequent maintenance of high levels of performance in recall situations. Increasingly therefore, tests of motor recall have been designed using simple tasks with low levels of initial learning and the testing of short term retention.

It would be inappropriate in this context to detail the evidence accumulating from research into memory for skills. It is relevant, however, to examine the relationship of proprioception to memory for motor tasks. In this chapter it has been made clear that proprioceptive feedback plays a role in learning of tasks. Even without evidence it would be logical to assume that in remembering skills it should also contribute. Attention to relevant patterns of proprioceptive stimulation has been stressed as a concomitant of learning. Attention cannot be directed in this way unless those patterns have been somehow stored or remembered. Some 'trace' or store of patterns of proprioceptive feedback must exist for comparison to be made with incoming stimulation; what Adams (1971) called the perceptual trace.

Before the evidence for the way in which memory processes operate is considered, it is necessary to briefly review current theoretical positions. In recent years two distinct kinds of theory have become popular (see Murdock, 1971, for a summary). Interference theory has been used to explain much of the data derived in verbal learning experiments. The assumption in interference theory is that learning occurs as a result of the formation of associations which develop through temporal contiguity and reinforcement. These associations are liable to extinction, however, when reinforcement ceases and may also suffer if new associations must be developed before the time of recall. Therefore, forgetting of first list associations when intervening lists have been learned (or retroactive inhibition) is produced as a result of extinction of responses through non-reinforcement and competition between original and interpolated responses. The retention of newly learned material may also be affected by prior learning (either experimentally produced or as a result of extra-laboratory experience). This phenomenon has become known as proactive inhibition.

This theory had its origins in the 1930s and was formulated as a result of the failure of the 'decay' hypothesis to account for many aspects of forgetting. The decay hypothesis suggests that an event in the environment leaves a neural trace and that forgetting comes about as a result of decay of the trace over time. The strength of the trace may be improved by repetition of the event which in turn reduces the rate of forgetting.

Alternative views of memory have developed from computer and communication sciences. These have generally become known as information-processing theories of memory. Perhaps the best known example of this kind of theory is that proposed by Atkinson and Shiffrin (1968). In their theory, described as the buffer model, information is seen as impinging on the organism's sense organs whereupon a series of stages of processing occur. There are thought to be three storage areas, a sensory store which holds information for a very short period of time (seconds only), a short-term store and a long-term store. Information is transmitted from one store to the next, but each store is liable to forgetting also, so that some of the information is lost. In the sensory store, information is lost due to decay, whereas forgetting may occur in short-term and long-term store both because of interference and a loss of accessibility. Located within the short-term store is a 'buffer' in which information is rehearsed before transmission to the long term store. The short-term store is considered to have a limited capacity.

Obviously, this description is an over-simplification, but it enables a more informed examination of the relevant experimental work. In general, the theoretical positions have been established on the basis of verbal learning phenomena and their adequacy has been measured by their capacity to explain forgetting in this context. Schmidt (1971) examined the evidence concerning the nature of forgetting in long term retention studies for both motor and verbal tasks. He claimed that interference effects are identical in the two kinds of memory tasks. Previous studies which have shown discrepancies between interference factors in verbal and motor memory (e.g. McAllister, 1952) may be reconciled when measurement artifacts are discounted.

Short-term retention studies in motor behaviour have beeen less consistent with information derived in the verbal learning tradition. Adams and Dijkstra (1966) examined short term memory for motor responses and found some results analogous to those in studies of verbal retention. Using a simple unseen linear arm movement, subjects were given varying numbers of training trials and recall was measured at various time intervals up to two minutes following the training. This experiment therefore required the subject to store proprioceptive information after a relatively low level of initial learning (1, 3, 6 to 15 trials) and reproduce the movement i.e. match the new information with that in store after a delay of up to two minutes. The results showed that errors increased as a function of length of retention interval. Errors decreased as number of initial trials increased. (See Fig. 17). In other words, Adams and Dijkstra found results similar to those in verbal short term memory (see Peterson and Peterson 1959). They pointed out that not only were the major effects the same, but also the slopes of the retention curves were the same for motor forgetting as for forgetting of verbal materials. The theoretical interpretation made by Adams and Dijkstra was that support was provided for a decay hypothesis of forgetting, but they acknowledged that the experiment was so designed as to provide little opportunity for proactive or retroactive interference to occur. They concluded: 'The mounting evidence for interference as the explanation of short-term verbal forgetting urges that we give full test of this view in the motor domain, although it is certainly hard to see any sources of interference for our simple motor responses.' Perhaps the obvious answer to this is that a whole life time of simple reaching movements may provide adequate proactive interference to produce the forgetting which they discovered.

Although Adams and Dijkstra were concerned with proprioceptive influences on retention they did not compare visual and proprioceptive influences. Posner and Konick (1966) and Posner (1967) have examined differences in the quality of memory for these two types of information. In

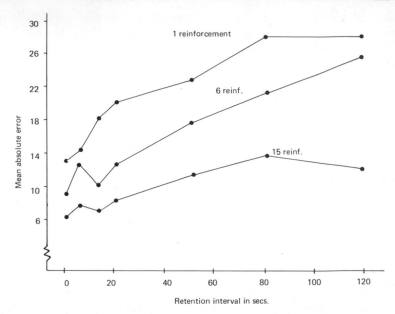

Fig. 17. Performance curves for the three reinforcement conditions as a function of retention interval (Adams and Dijkstra, J. Exp. Psychol. 71, 314-318. copyright 1966 by the American Psychological Association. Reprinted by permission.)

both of these studies the orientation of the experiment was towards an information processing view of memory.

Posner and Konick (1966) used two tasks. In the visual-location task the subjects were required to reproduce the position of a circle along a line. In the proprioceptive task, subjects moved a lever a given distance whilst unable to see their hands and were then required to reproduce the distance moved by moving a different lever which had a different starting position. The results of this study indicated that similarities existed between the visual-location test of memory and verbal retention, i.e. little forgetting occurred during the retention interval when that interval was unfilled, but when interpolated activity was introduced, significant forgetting occurred (retroactive inhibition). Posner and Konick (1966) interpreted the evidence in information processing terms as being a function of the amount of processing capacity available during the interval.

In the proprioceptive task, however, forgetting or decrement in performance was found even where there was no interpolated activity, which would be predicted on the basis of the Adams and Dijkstra (1966) result. Also, when interpolated activity was introduced the amount of forgetting was not a function of the difficulty of the interpolated task. The inclusion of an interpolated task, therefore, produced a significant difference in the quality of retention of proprioceptive and visual/verbal tasks. This indicated to Posner that visual and proprioceptive short term memory may involve entirely different central processing requirements. In an attempt to clarify this issue Posner (1967) performed an experiment which was designed to allow separation between modality effects and effects due to the type of information i.e. location and distance information. He used four groups two of which performed with vision, and two without. The groups were identified as visual location, visual distance, kinaesthetic location and kinaesthetic distance. The movement task consisted again of moving a lever through a specified distance and reproducing this movement on a second lever. The difference between distance and location conditions was that for location the starting positions were identical for the two levers whereas for distance the starting positions varied. All groups experienced either no interval or a twenty second interval between the original movement and its recall and the interval was either taken up with an interpolated classificatory task or was simply rest.

The results of this study are illustrated in Figs 18 and 19. There were no significant differences between conditions where there was no interval between learning trial and recall. This, in itself, is quite a surprising result. In the visual conditions the subjects were obtaining both proprioceptive and visual information and yet did not perform significantly better than with proprioceptive information alone. There were, however, significant effects due to the interval of twenty seconds where all groups showed an increase in errors after this interval except the visual-location group when the time interval was unfilled. What is more important for the current discussion is that interpolated activity had a different effect on visual compared with non visual retention. Decrements in performance occurred following interpolated activity for the visual group, whereas little decrement occurred for the visual group without interpolated activity. A decrement in retention was observed for the non-visual group whether the retention interval contained interpolated activity or not. Posner (1967) interpreted the results in the following way. The interpolated task acts to control central processing capacity or attention which is available during the time interval. Where available central processing capacity is involved in a secondary task, the opportunity for rehearsal is reduced. In the visual tasks this rehearsal is important and a reduction in the available processing capacity therefore causes a larger error score. In the proprioceptive tasks there is a decrement in performance (forgetting) whether or not the interval is unfilled. The availability of processing capacity makes no difference. This interpretation seems to fit in well with what has been said previously concerning proprioception and the conscious/unconscious dichotomy. If only a small proportion of the proprioceptive stimuli are directly transmitted to cortical centres the influence of the amount of attentional

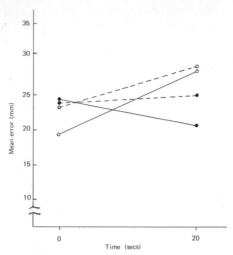

Fig. 18. Mean error of reproduction as a function of recall interval for visual information. The four groups were: location with rest (•—•), location with interpolated activity (•—•), distance with rest (○---•) and distance with interpolated activity (○---•) (M. I. Posner. J. Exp. Psychol., 75, 103-107. Copyright 1967 by the American Psychological Association. Reprinted by permission.)

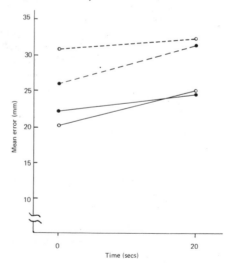

Fig. 19. Mean error of reproduction as a function of recall interval for proprioceptive information. The four groups were: location with rest (•—•), location with interpolated activity (○—○), distance with rest (•---•) and distance with interpolated activity (○---○) (M. I. Posner. J. Exp. Psychol., 75, 103-107, Copyright 1967 by the American Psychological Association. Reprinted by permission.)

capacity available is likely to be small, compared with vision where a large proportion of stimuli are processed at a conscious level. In other words, retention mechanisms for proprioceptive stimuli may differ markedly from retention mechanisms for verbal and/or visual stimuli.

This result also provides some support for the decay hypothesis for motor responses advanced by Adams and Dijkstra (1966). If interpolated activity has no influence on proprioceptive recall, retroactive interference can be dismissed as a contributory factor in forgetting. This still does not obviate the possibility that proactive interference is responsible for some of the decrement. Posner (1967) also pointed out that his evidence merely revealed distinctions between the proprioceptive and visual memory systems, but did not provide evidence for the physiological bases of these differences.

There is some contradictory evidence against Posner's position. Blick and Bilodeau (1963) presented subjects with an arc drawing task and found no significant effect on retention when an interpolated task was given, but support is expressed by Boswell and Bilodeau (1964). In their experiment subjects were required to reproduce a movement after a delay of 28 seconds. During this interval one group was required to pick up a pencil which 'accidentally' fell to the floor. This group produced inferior results in the recall of the movement to those who had no such activity during the interval.

In a recent study, Keele and Ellis (1972) proposed that discrepancies between results may be a function of different aspects of proprioception having different retention characteristics. Cutaneous, tendonous, muscular and the various arthroidal receptors may all contribute to the total memory of a movement. There is no guarantee that each of these sensory inputs is stored in the same way nor that forgetting processes are identical for each type of input. Since studies of motor memory have tended to use different movements, in which these sensory sources have had different emphases, it is not surprising that inconsistencies in the results have occurred. Keele (1968) also reminded investigators that proprioception cannot be considered a single 'sense'.

Zahorick (1972) described a related problem. If retroactive paradigms are employed, the nature of the cues in learning an interpolated activity may have significant effects. She suggested that interference is likely to be greatest where similar cues are used by the subject in order to complete the interpolated task as well as the original task. In her experiment subjects learned an initial task and were trained to use either positional or distance proprioceptive cues. The interpolated task required half the subjects from each group to learn a new movement using either positional or distance cues. Recall and relearning of the original task showed that interference was greater where the interpolated movement had been learned using similar cues to the original movement. Since some tasks may be learned on the basis of different kinds of cues, Zahorick pointed out that 'Interference in motor learning is not only a function of the nature of the interfering task, but is also a function of the strategy that subjects adopt in learning the task'.

These methodological problems await further investigation. It is clear that both specificity of proprioceptive retention and the possibility that subjects use different strategies for learning may significantly affect retention studies and may even demand the re-interpretation of some of the earlier work in the long term retention of motor skills.

In spite of some contradictions, however, the general trend amongst those involved in motor skill research has been to postulate independent memory mechanisms for proprioceptive and visual retention. In contrast, some authorities working in the short-term retention of verbal material have found cause to invoke proprioceptive feedback as a hypothetical construct in order to explain some phenomena in their field. This position is epitomised by the work of Hintzman (1965, 1967) who suggested that proprioceptive feedback is used in the short-term storage of visually perceived items. Items which are presented visually may have some degree of acoustic similarity for the observer. It has been demonstrated that there is greater confusion in the retention of words or other verbal items if they are acoustically similar than if they are dissimilar. This has been interpreted as indicating that storage must therefore take the form of some kind of acoustic image. Hintzman (1967) maintained that an alternative hypothesis is possible. If a subject rehearses a verbal item subvocally when it is presented, minute muscular contractions will occur providing proprioceptive feedback. This feedback may then be monitored for retrieval. (The assumption that sub-vocal articulation leads to muscular contraction in the vocal apparatus has its origin in the work of Watson (1926) whose view was that 'thought' consisted of these muscular movements). Hintzman (1967) suggested that in a large proportion of cases acoustic similarity would be paralleled by similarity in proprioceptive feedback from the muscular contractions of sub-vocal rehearsal. Either hypothesis may therefore be tenable. In an ingenious experiment Hintzman (1967) sought to test the adequacy of the two hypotheses by testing the short-term retention of verbal materials which were acoustically similar but which differed in the 'place of articulation', i.e. the front, middle or back of the mouth. No difference in confusion would be predicted for these verbal items on acoustic grounds. On the basis of the proprioceptive feedback hypothesis, since different muscles would be involved in the sub-vocal rehearsal, it would be predicted that items articulated in the same place would be more easily confused. His experiment provided support for this position.

On the one hand, some evidence exists for proprioceptive short-term memory being independent of other kinds of short-term memory and on the other hand it appears possible that proprioception may form a key part of other forms of short-term memory.

6

PROPRIOCEPTION AND THE TIMING OF MOTOR RESPONSES

6 PROPRIOCEPTION AND THE TIMING OF MOTOR RESPONSES

Introduction

In a large proportion of physical skills the identification of relevant stimuli and the accurate production of appropriate responses is insufficient for high levels of performance. The timing with which a response is initiated is of equal importance in the determination of quality of performance. This is true both in continuous as well as discrete skills. The timing of a response is particularly important in sports skills. Knapp (1963) has emphasised that the concept of timing in sports skill is extremely complex. The term has different connotations depending upon the task. In some skills the major function of timing is to produce a mechanically optimum 'flow' of responses. For example, in javelin throwing, discus or shot put, good timing consists of triggering a sequence of responses according to some model of mechanical efficiency. Knapp pointed out, however, that good timing in skills which require a prolonged series of identical responses, such as long-distance swimming, may be assessed rather by the capacity of the performer to order his efforts or spurts of activity so as to produce maximum advantage over opponents. The problem is further complicated in some sports skills since the tempo of the activity may be under the control of the performer himself. In other words, a performer with 'good timing' may be able to manufacture for himself advantageous conditions for responding. This is the case in racquet games for example, where the performer who has timed his movements well will find himself well balanced and with sufficient time to make careful responses.

The experimental capacity to deal with these different kinds of real-life situations is extremely limited. Evidence has accumulated for only the timing of very simple responses, where conditions may be adequately controlled. The experimental investigations have normally been concerned with identifying factors which influence the temporal initiation of an individual movement after some predetermined interval. This chapter is concerned with the evidence which has been produced concerning the phenomenon of timing simple responses and two of the theories which have invoked proprioceptive feedback as a component process in the timing of motor behaviour.

In the course of Chapter Five, it was pointed out that patterns of proprioceptive feedback may be thought of in a temporal sense and that the initial components of a pattern may act as stimuli to activity or respond. The identification of a temporal pattern through learning is likely to enable the skilled performer to respond more quickly within that situation than the novice. The skilled performer has acquired the capacity to anticipate future situations. Of course, this anticipation may occur also on the basis of information derived in other modalities. The identification of visual cues is likely to have the same effect in permitting anticipation to occur. These anticipatory timing situations may be viewed as essentially similar, differing only in the modality through which stimulation is derived. On the other hand it is possible to consider the two kinds of anticipation as distinct from each other and differing in fundamental ways. The latter is the view expressed by Poulton (1957). He distinguished between receptor anticipation and perceptual anticipation. Receptor anticipation is said to occur when the subject is capable of reviewing the stimuli to which responses must be made at a later time through the use of exteroceptors. In this case prior experience within the specific task situation may not be of crucial importance. For example, a total novice at tennis may be quite capable of hitting a tennis ball lobbed slowly towards him. The subject has sufficient experience in the anticipation of moving objects that he is capable of performing the task of hitting the ball with relative ease. Poulton (1957) pointed out that the subject must be aware of his movement time, however. The accuracy of his response in terms of the direction achieved, or in the anticipation of a spinning or fast ball does require specific practice of course.

In Poulton's analysis, perceptual anticipation is found where no preview of the stimulus is possible exteroceptively, but the events themselves occur in predictable fashion, so that once the sequence of events has been learned, subjects may anticipate future events without reference to external inform-ation. In this case the anticipation is likely to be highly specific to the task in question.

Poulton's (1957) analysis may be criticized on two grounds. Firstly, it proposes a dichotomy where none need exist. If it is assumed that the internal timing mechanisms for perceptual anticipation are basically proprio-ceptive then the distinction between the two distinguishes only differences in modality. At the same time it is misleading to label one form of anticipation as perceptual and the other as receptor, which implies that there is a distinction between the two situations in terms of their perceptual demands. Perhaps both types of anticipation rely on perception and both rely on receptor activity.

These criticisms depend for their validity upon the accuracy of the statement that proprioception is the basis upon which internal anticipation occurs, i.e. anticipation not based on exteroceptive preview. The evidence for this point is discussed later, but it must first be pointed out that receptor and perceptual anticipation as defined by Poulton (1957) need not be found mutually exclusively in one task. Anticipatory behaviour may change within a given task as a result of learning. In a two hand coordination tracking task where preview of stimuli is available, anticipation may occur on the basis of exteroceptive cues at first. After learning, the internal mechanisms of anticipation may be used, releasing visual attention for other purposes; a restatement of the Fitts hypothesis (see Chapter Four) from the point of view of the timing of responses.

Evidence for Proprioception and Timing Behaviour

A most detailed review of the evidence in this field has been made by Schmidt (1971). He noted that the value of proprioception in timing is amply demonstrated at an anecdotal level. The musician tapping his foot generates proprioceptive feedback which is apparently useful in keeping time. We 'keep time' by tapping fingers or feet in observing regular or predictable events.

Interest in the use of proprioception in estimating elapsed time is by no means new. James (1890) discussed the nature of proprioception's usefulness in this context and cited the work of Münsterberg (1889). It was Münsterberg's contention that in estimating the duration of elapsed time subjects would depend upon proprioceptive stimulation from movements occurring during the interval. In more recent times, support for this position has been produced by Goldstone, Boardman and Lhamon (1958). In their study, subjects were required to estimate a fairly lengthy time span. Their accuracy in determining the duration of a 30 second time period was noted under various conditions. In one situation, subjects were allowed to count aloud and produced best results with this technique. When subjects were required to count sub-vocally it was found that performance was poorer. Goldstone et al suggested that the difference was probably due to the influence of proprioceptive feedback. Counting aloud produced substantially greater amounts of feedback than counting sub-vocally. Although subjects were required not to make any movements when counting sub-vocally the authors noted that many subjects, particularly in younger age groups, violated these instructions and indulged in foot and finger tapping. No formal check was reported on the effectiveness of these strategies, but Goldstone, Boardman and Lhamon (1958) assumed that they served to enhance proprioceptive stimulation. At least subjects evidently considered that this behaviour served to increase their level of performance in the timing task. Goldstone et al agreed that prior knowledge of the meaning of 30 seconds was necessary for the successful completion of the task. Obviously this kind of knowledge develops with age. It is not surprising that it was found that younger children produced inferior performances in the estimation of time irrespective of the amount of proprioceptive feedback. They suggested that at about eight years of age, after which age performance approached adult levels, proprioceptive cues become associated with standard temporal concepts providing a part of the mechanism for temporal conceptualization. In the same way, duration may be calibrated partly on the basis of proprioception. The authors did not suggest what the other 'parts of the mechanism' may be, nor did they relate their work to timing in motor skill activities. However, this paper stimulated those more specifically involved in motor skill research to review the possibility that proprioceptive cues might have a more general timing function rather than the simple estimation of elapsed time. In one sense this study itself may be thought of as applying to motor skills since the end of an estimated elapsed time was signalled by the motor response of arm raising. In other words, subjects were required to perform a response at a specific point in time and their accuracy in so doing was increased by additional proprioceptive feedback.

Goldstone, Boardman and Lhamon (1958) did not speculate on the neural mechanisms by which proprioceptive mechanisms may facilitate time keeping. However, Adams and Xhignesse (1960) suggested that the proprioceptive feedback circuits outlined by Ruch (1951) and discussed in Chapter Two might provide adequate bases for time estimation. Schmidt (1971) came to the conclusion that there is good evidence to suppose that in motor behaviour proprioceptive cues form the basis of timing. He distinguished, however, between two distinct hypotheses concerning the mechanisms by which proprioceptive feedback may fulfil this function. These two hypotheses may now be reviewed in detail.

Input Hypothesis of Proprioceptive Function in Timing

Adams (1968) severely criticized S-R chaining theories of learning. These theories claim that feedback from the previous response acts as the stimulus for the next response. Adams noted that this explanation was inadequate to explain very high speed movements in which feedback is too slow to act as the stimulus for the next movement. He went on, '. . . The proprioceptive cue for, say, movement C need not be from the immediately preceding movement B which . . . is travelling too slowly to account for the speed with which C occurs. The cue could be from movement A which has had time to reach the brain.' (Adams, 1968, pp. 499). Schmidt (1971) re-interpreted this conclusion in terms of timing and suggested that the input hypothesis extended this view. Rather than saying that the proprioceptive feedback contains the stimulus to which a response is learned, the input hypothesis maintains that the feedback contains the stimuli by means of which the response is timed. Although this interpretation makes an important distinction between timing and learning it begs certain questions. For example, does not timing also need to be learned? By suggesting that proprioceptive cues serve in timing behaviour does not deny that series of S-R connections are still being formed and are still effectively chains of behaviour. In other words, some of Adams' criticisms of S-R chaining theories of learning may apply equally well to S-R chaining theories of the timing of behaviour.

Schmidt summarised the input hypothesis in the following way: 'This view maintains that if a subject is required to make a series of timed responses, he uses the proprioceptive feedback from some earlier portion of the sequence to trigger a later portion of the response' (Schmidt, 1971). The hypothesis may be illustrated by referring to laboratory tasks which require cyclical series of movements of a predictable nature such as use of a rotary pursuitmeter. In this situation, temporal patterns of proprioceptive feedback become learned as the rotary arm movements are practised over extended trials. Changes of direction in arm movement may therefore come to be timed by prior stimulus elements from within the total pattern. Obviously, the stimulus configuration which immediately precedes the change in direction of movement and its associated muscular activity cannot fulfil this function since nervous system transmission lags in time would result in the overshooting of the action. Transmission delay would result in the delayed onset of the new muscular action. The hypothesis may also be applied in many every-day tasks. Schmidt (1971) used the example of pedalling a bicycle, where changes in the muscular activity may be signalled in like manner. One could suggest that the timing of a movement's components may occur similarly in swimming, discus throwing, even running and walking, and any other gross motor sports skills in which there exists a regular cycle of activity.

It may be noted at this point that according to the evidence presented by Laszlo (1967) some criticisms of this hypothesis are possible. Laszlo found (it will be remembered from Chapter Four) that the total disruption of proprioceptive feedback had relatively little impact on finger tapping responses which on any superficial basis would appear to be the kind of activity in which timing, of the kind noted by Schmidt, is most likely to occur. It may be recalled that Laszlo's interpretation of her findings was that a motor programming explanation of movement rather than explanations based on proprioceptive feedback is more acceptable for movements involving rate (Laszlo 1971). However, as pointed out in the previous chapter, the alternatives may not be necessarily mutually exclusive if it is assumed that overlearning results in a change from proprioceptive control to motor programming. Certainly there appears to be evidence which supports the input hypothesis of timing in motor behaviour.

Schmidt (1971) listed the following predictions which may be derived from the input hypothesis.

1. There should exist an inverse relation between rate of change in proprioceptive feedback and temporal lag in triggering response mechanisms. To look at extreme positions: no cuing function would be hypothesized from constant proprioceptive feedback whereas highly accurate cuing should be possible when the proprioceptive feedback is constantly changing. Some issue may be taken with this prediction in its general format. The rate of change of information may not be of critical importance for the whole task. Provided that rate of change in information occurs at that point in time where new responding is to be initiated it will serve equally well. It might be predicted that overall high rates of change in informtmation may even cause less efficient learning since identification of the specific element of the stimulus pattern to which response should be made may be more difficult for the learner.

2. If proprioceptive feedback is varied from trial to trial, temporal pattern recognition will become more difficult and a corresponding reduction occur in the accuracy of timing responses. Conversely, increasing the similarity of proprioceptive feedback over trials should result in greater accuracy in the timing of responses. Therefore, if different movements occur prior to an identical response, the timing of that identical response will be inferior.

3. By increasing the force and amplitude of movement, a corresponding increase in proprioceptive discharge should occur enabling more accurate timing of responses. Again this prediction is not perhaps directly derivable from the input hypothesis. The hypothesis does not contend that the saliency of the feedback is relevant, merely that it be present. One could argue that provided the proprioceptive feedback reaches cortical levels, the intensity of proprioceptive discharge should make relatively little difference. Appreciation of the stimulus is all that should be necessary for the subject to use the temporal pattern as a cue for timing new elements of the response. It is, however, in the context of this prediction that the majority of the evidence for the input hypothesis has accumulated. Schmidt (1971) quoted Bahrick's (1957) study in support of this aspect. This study was discussed in Chapter Four and it will be remembered that Bahrick found increased accuracy in lever control when the lever was operated isotonically rather than iso-metrically. Schmidt does not however mention that contradictory results were discussed by Gibbs (1965) and North and Lomnicki (1961). Also, it may be pointed out that in the Bahrick (1957) study, proprioceptive feedback may have differed significantly in terms of the degree of cortical stimulation under the two conditions. In isometric activity there is but little movement around the joints whereas in isotonic activity there is considerable feedback from these proprioceptors. It has been pointed out repeatedly (see

Chapter Two) that joint and not muscular proprioceptors have direct links to the cortex. Therefore, the superiority of the isotonic group in timing may be simply a function of the fact that conscious awareness and cuing occurred in that case and not in the case of the isometric group.

Evidence which may also be thought of as partly contradictory, is available from a study of Adams and Creamer (1962) in which they considered performance in a step tracking task. In this task subjects were required to use a control lever in order to maintain a pointer between two lines. The lines appeared on alternate sides of the display and changed sides every two or four seconds. The subject was therefore forced to anticipate the switch and move the pointer as rapidly as possible to the new position. In this study the nature of proprioceptive feedback was manipulated by varying the spring tension on the control and the amplitude of movement of the lever required to change the pointer from one side to the display to the other. The results of this experiment indicated that increasing the spring tension produced greater accuracy in the timing of responses, whereas changes in amplitude of movement did not produce significant effects. This evidence supports the hypothesis in part in that increased muscular tension and hence more intense proprioceptive discharge caused superior timing of the responses. However, the fact that amplitude of movement did not produce significant differences contradicts the third prediction of the input hypothesis. Schmidt (1971) maintained that two possible explanations are available for this contradiction. Firstly, by the nature of the task, no movement was actually occurring for a period of time before switching the pointer to opposite sides of the display. The subjects made the change and maintained their new position until the time for the next movement. Therefore, the greater range of movement would be of little benefit to the timing since it had terminated prior to the initiation of the new response. Secondly, it was suggested that a mechanical advantage lay in having smaller movements of the control. Thus the benefit derived from increasing amplitude of movement for timing purposes was more than counter-balanced by the mechanical disadvantage of the increased amplitude. Both of these seem acceptable interpretations of the discrepancy between prediction 3 of the input hypothesis and the results of the Adams and Creamer experiment.

A somewhat different type of experiment, but one which also has a bearing on the third prediction, was performed by Grose (1967). Grose required subjects to produce a response when two pointers were aligned. Three subgroups were used who were required to make different responses at the point of alignment. In one case, subjects were required merely to lift a finger from a key, another group was required to move the arm a distance of two feet and a final group walked 9 feet and kicked over a barrier. In support of the input hypothesis prediction 3, there was shown to be a decrease in error with increasing size of movement. Also, consistency of performance was found to increase with greater amplitude of movement. Schmidt (1971) noted that the results were confounded in several ways. No attempt was made in the study of Grose (1967) to separate the effects of movement time, complexity and proprioceptive characteristics. Although providing evidence for the input hypothesis it is by no means conclusive. In a series of experiments attempts have been made to control these variables to provide clearer support for prediciton 3 of the input hypothesis. Notable amongst these are the experiments of Ellis, Schmidt and Wade (1968), Ellis (1969), and Schmidt and Christina (1969). Ellis, Schmidt and Wade (1968), in an experiment which in some respects paralleled that of Adams and Creamer (1962), manipulated force and amplitude in a timing task. Subjects were required to move a sliding marker along a track completing the total movement in exactly 2 seconds. The length of the track was either 2.5 or 65.0 centimeters and the loading on the slide was either 0 or 8.5 pounds. In direct contradiction to the results of Adams and Creamer (1962), Ellis, Schmidt and Wade (1968) found a significant effect of amplitude of movement and no effect due to increasing the force required to move the slide. No explanation was given for this contradiction by Ellis, Schmidt and Wade (1968). Partial support is again provided from this experiment for the hypothesis. It will be noted that in this experiment velocity and amplitude were confounded. Using a more complex experimental design, however, Ellis (1969) found greater support for the input hypothesis. Lever manipulation was required in this task and velocity, acceleration, viscous resistance and tension of the lever were varied. In addition subjects were required to spell two, three and four letter words during the movement of the lever. Although all of the results were not significant, the general trend was in favour of the third prediction of the input hypothesis. An increase in proprioceptive feedback caused either by increasing muscular effort or amplitude and velocity, produced increasing accuracy in the timing of movements. Like Grose (1967), Ellis (1969) also found that the subjects with greater proprioceptive feedback also improved in consistency as well as in mean accuracy. The influence of spelling longer rather than shorter words improved timing and Ellis made the point (like Goldstone, Boardman and Lhamon, 1958) that the greater proprioceptive feedback from the vocal apparatus of spelling the longer words provided a superior basis for timing. Ellis (1969) also used a control group for which no movement occurred during the timed interval. This group did, however, experience the secondary spelling task. In a post-test in which the spelling task was removed there was a marked deterioration in the performance of this group. Ellis noted that the deterioration was much greater than when the spelling task was removed for other groups. The inference was made that alternative proprioceptive feedback could be relied upon for the movement groups. This inference raises one interesting point; the nature of the cues to which response may be made in a real-life gross motor situation may vary from individual to individual and also depend upon the exigencies of a particular situation. Performers may change their timing cues with little detriment to performance.

Schmidt (1971) pointed out that: 'Although these studies seem to implicate proprioceptive feedback in timing somehow, there is a methodological problem that prevents such a strong conclusion. In each case, the proprioceptive feedback was manipulated by changing the dynamics of the control, and thereby changing the proprioceptive feedback may have also created a mechanically more favourable system for responding.' (Schmidt, 1971, pp. 387). Schmidt was careful to acknowledge that the same reason which may have explained the negative results of the Adams and Creamer (1962) experiment may also have assisted in providing the positive results in the other experiments.

The problem was circumvented in a study by Schmidt and Christina (1969) in which the ingenious alternative was used of providing differing degrees of proprioceptive feedback to a limb not involved in the major task. The subjects were divided into three groups each of which had to anticipate without preview the alignment of two pointers which occurred every 1.50 seconds, and respond with the right hand. One group acted as a control, whereas the two other groups experienced either small scale rotary movements or large scale rotary movements in the left arm during the timed interval. Both the movement groups showed superior performance compared with the control in the timing task. However, according to prediction 3 of the input hypothesis, the larger movement should have produced significantly better timing performance, and this was not the case. This may be explained to some extent by the inconsistency of the large scale left arm movement. Schmidt and Christina (1969) discovered that the subjects using small scale movements were far more consistent in those movements. This finding is indirectly relevant to the second prediction of the input hypothesis, namely that variations in proprioceptive feedback prior to identical responses should provide an inferior basis for anticipation. Better and more direct evidence would require that the two movements were of different size, but with no variations in the consistency with which the movements were executed.

Similar contradictory evidence was found by Christina (1970). In this case linear rather than rotary arm movements were used for the left hand and the right hand was used for the major response task. Subjects were assigned to one of five treatment combinations. The influence upon timing was tested between subjects with minimal proprioceptive feedback versus those with moderate and maximum proprioceptive feedback. Magnitude of feedback was manipulated in terms of both size and force of movement. Only subjects receiving maximum proprioceptive feedback performed the right hand timing task with greater consistency than subjects receiving a minimal level. These results contradict Schmidt and Christina's (1969) finding.

To date therefore, the evidence for the input hypothesis is extremely confusing. Only one of the predictions from the hypothesis has been directly tested and no clear result has so far been derived. It remains for further research to show whether predictions 1 and 2 find empirical support. These predictions were that rate of change of proprioceptive feedback should be inversely related to timing accuracy and that variations in pre-response proprioceptive feedback should result in inferior timing performance.

Perhaps one of the most important problems in this field of research is the possibility that subjects use idiosyncratic cues. This point was emphasized by Christina (1970) in a consideration of the role of attention in the timing task. Christina found that 43 per cent of subjects moving the left arm control during the timing interval tended to covary the velocity of that movement with the time of the right hand response. Similar reports were noted by Schmidt and Christina (1969). Christina (1970) suggested that this group of subjects probably attended to the proprioceptive cues whereas the remainder either used the proprioceptive feedback differently or perhaps used a purely cognitive strategy such as counting.

Decay Hypothesis

The alternative to the input hypothesis has been called the decay hypothesis. This is related to the decay theory of forgetting (see Hall, 1966, for a summary). In its original form the decay theory of forgetting suggested that information which has been stored by a learner will gradually become unavailable. At a physiological level this may be conceptualized as a fading or decay of the memory trace. Quite obviously this theory is inadequate to account for many of the phenomena associated with memory in general. Purely temporal variables cannot account for the ways in which some items may be remembered over long periods of time. Experimentally the decay theory was initially discredited through the work of Jenkins and Dallenbach (1924). McGeoch's (1932) subsequent paper established that disuse or decay was not a primary source of forgetting and interference occurring between learning and recall has since received much greater support as the major cause of loss in retention. However, within the last decade distinctions between perceptual trace, short-term and long term memory have brought about a reconsideration of decay effects. The development of new methods of investigation have enabled tests of retention to be made over periods of one second or less. Sperling (1960) for example found significant differences between 'retention' intervals of under one second and those over one second. Similarly, a new methodology devised by Peterson and Peterson (1959) showed retention changes over intervals of three to eighteen seconds (short term memory). Although contradictory evidence is available (see Jung 1968 for a review), it seems quite likely that the decay of memory traces may have a significant impact on retention levels in very short-term memory. Sperling (1967) suggested that a transfer occurs from a peripheral store in which sensory inputs may remain for about half a second, into a central store where the material may be rehearsed to prevent forgetting. If this transference does not occur decay of the material results in forgetting, and absence of rehearsal results in the loss of material from the central store.

This concept was applied to proprioception by Adams and Xhignesse (1960) who suggested that after any response has occurred, proprioceptive stimulation is temporally stored. They hypothesized that the stimulation then decays over time in some predictable way. It was their contention that this decay could be used by the subject in order to time future responses. The decay with time may act as the interval standard by which duration is judged. The distinction between this hypothesis and the input hypothesis should be emphasized. Whereas the input view stresses the fact that feedback from a prior response acts as a stimulus for a later one, the decay hypothesis suggests that it is the decay of this stimulation in short term storage which acts as the cue. This distinction therefore causes different predictions to be made. Unlike the input hypothesis, movement need not be occurring immediately prior to the response in order for the proprioceptive feedback to function. Although movement may have ceased before the response to be timed occurs, the decay of the stimulation derived from the last response may still be available for timing purposes. Since this decay occurs over a very limited period of time, however, the period of inactivity before the timed response cannot be too great. Schmidt (1971) suggested that the rate of decay is non-linear and possibly may be exponential. He did not present evidence for this and in studies on the decay of visual information it has not proved possible to determine whether the decay is exponential or linear.

Other predictions are also possible on the basis of the decay hypothesis. Unfortunately a proportion of these predictions are identical with those derivable from the input hypothesis and do not therefore serve to support either one hypothesis or the other. For example, both hypotheses would predict that inconsistency of prior responding would result in deterioration of the timed response. In terms of the decay hypothesis, this would result from the differences in decay characteristics of proprioceptive stimuli from dissimilar preceding responses. Similarly, both hypotheses predict that the magnitude of preceding responses will be directly proportional to the accuracy of timed responses. Since the timing of a motor response in decay terms depends on a rate of change in decay of a stimulus trace and if the decay is exponential, a more intense stimulus, provided by increased magnitude of a preceding response, should provide a 'larger' trace held in short term memory store and thereby a greater rate of decay, to be used as a cue for the next response. Timing accuracy of the subsequent response should be increased.

Schmidt (1971) listed a third prediction. This prediction stems only from the decay hypothesis. If decay is exponential then responding accuracy should be inversely related to the interval between a preceding response and the response to be timed. This prediction may be derived in the following way. The rate of decay of a stimulus trace from a preceding response is greater immediately after that response than after a delay. If decay follows a negatively accelerated curve, greater rate of decay is available for cuing functions immediately following a response, than after a delay. Should the negatively accelerated curve of decay reach asymptote before the initiation of the timed response then no difference would be predicted between this condition and a condition with no proprioceptive feedback; there being no rate of change information available for cuing functions.

Adams and Creamer (1962) tested this prediction of the decay hypothesis. Movements were to be made by subjects with no preview at predetermined intervals of two and four seconds. The results of their study indicated that superior timing of responses occurred with the shorter interval. This was seen by Adams and Creamer (1962) as support for the decay hypothesis. It is not, however, clear that subjects were using the decay of proprioceptive stimulation. Schmidt (1971) pointed out that the same result could have been achieved if subjects were using some 'cognitive' estimate such as counting. One could also speculate that subjects responded in some way minimally to provide proprioceptive input, by which timing could take place; analogous to the surreptitious finger-tapping in the Goldstone, Boardman and Lhamon (1958) experiment. Generally speaking, however, the evidence provided by Adams and Creamer has been viewed as support for the decay hypothesis. A further criticism of the Adams and Creamer experiment was made by Christina (1970). '(Adams and Creamer) . . . explained their findings by suggesting that the decaying proprioceptive trace has a more efficacious cuing character for a shorter duration than for a longer one. However, proprioceptive after-effects generated from moving the control prior to the interval were confounded with proprioceptive feedback from static arm tension during the interval, and thus it is difficult to determine whether the more proficient anticipatory responding to the 2 second interval was due to the after-effects, the static tension feedback, or some combination of both.' (Christina, 1970, pp. 126). For this reason Christina produced a new test of the decay hypothesis in which there was an absence of movement during the interval to be timed. Subjects were required to perform a left arm movement before the onset of the interval (2 seconds) and make a key release response with the right hand. The magnitude and load (tension) of left arm movement was either minimal, moderate or maximal. The results indicated that no significant differences existed under the three conditions, whereas the decay hypothesis would predict increasing accuracy for the three conditions in the order mentioned above. However, two criticisms can be made concerning this experiment. In the first place, subjects were also required to say the letters ABC during the timed interval, 'To control for any differnetial verbal effects on anticipatory performance . . .' Christina (1970) considered it possible that subjects may have used this source of feedback which was constant across conditions in order to time the interval. Certainly this aspect of the experiment devalues the negative evidence for the decay hypothesis. Secondly, although attempts were made by the experimenter to control rate of movement of the left arm, discrepancies in rate of left arm movement occurred over trials. In other words, subjects may have received inconsistent feedback prior to the timed interval which would serve to reduce the accuracy of the timed response.

A solution to this methodological problem was found by Quesada and Schmidt (1970). Instead of relying on pre-training to produce consistent active movements of the left arm, they used passively induced movement, in which the subject's left arm was moved by a motor driven handle towards the body and came to rest on the arm of a chair. The result was that the duration of movement and presumably the proprioceptive stimulation derived from it was consistent over trials. In their experiment two groups were used. Both were required to time a two second interval and respond as accurately as possible without preview. The experimental group experienced the movement prior to the two second interval. The movement of the handle could be observed by the control group but they did not experience the movement. Both groups had forty trials in which knowledge of results was given. Subjects who experienced movement showed significantly greater accuracy in the timing response. There was less within subject variability and algebraic and absolute errors were smaller for this group. Subjects were retested after a week and at this time a further ten trials with knowledge of results were given to both groups and twenty trials with no knowledge of results. (Christina, 1970, gave knowledge of results consistently throughout his experiment). In the Quesada and Schmidt (1970) study it was found that during the period of absence of knowledge of results there remained a significant difference between the two groups. Those experiencing the movement showed both greater consistency and smaller absolute errors. Both parts of the study therefore provided support for the decay hypothesis and directly contradicted the findings of Christina (1970). The results of this experiment are shown in Figures 20 and 21. Although these results show smaller errors for the movement group it is also apparent that improvement in timing accuracy also occurred for the group without movement. Quesada and Schmidt did not speculate on the possible reasons for this improvement, but since no movement occurred in the interval to be timed it must be assumed that these

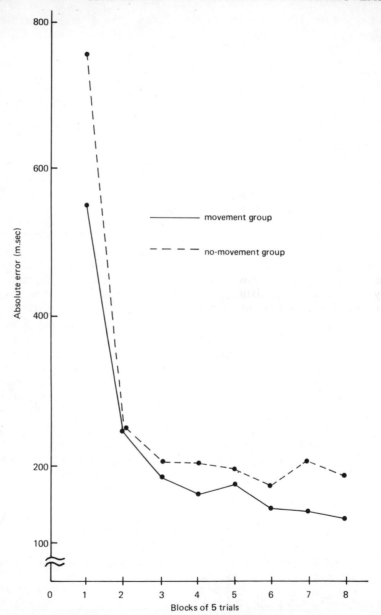

Fig. 20. *Average absolute error for groups with and without proprioceptive feedback prior to the timed interval (Quesada and Schmidt, 1970).*

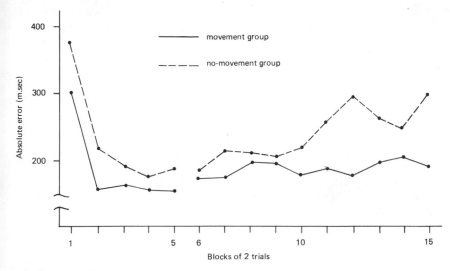

Fig. 21. Average absolute error for groups with and without proprioceptive feedback prior to the timed interval. Trial blocks 1-5 with knowledge of results (KR), trial blocks 6-15 without KR (Quesada and Schmidt, 1970).

subjects were able to improve by means of cognitive strategies such as counting. It is also interesting to speculate whether absence of knowledge of results throughout the experiment, except that inherent within the situation, would still reveal differences between the groups. It is possible that knowledge of results via the experimenter is essential for subjects to identify that point in the decay pattern at which the response should be made, although this is not a part of the decay hypothesis.

There appears at the moment to be insufficient evidence for any firm choice to be made between the two hypotheses. There is slightly more support for the input hypothesis but this hypothesis can not account for the evidence just discussed from Quesada and Schmidt. It is also possible that both hypotheses are correct. Earlier it was mentioned that Christina (1970) speculated on the basis of correlational data from left hand movement position and right hand accuracy in responding, that about half of his subjects were using one technique whereas the other half may have used cognitive methods. One could extend this argument and suggest that in real-life situations both proprioceptive decay and input information may be available and subjects may use either depending upon both the task and their previous experience within skill situations. The demands of any particular task may determine the timing strategy employed. Similarly, where individual differences exist in the same task, these may be a product of individual experience in timing techniques. It would be interesting to consider this hypothesis in an experimental setting. Overlearning trials, for example, given on a timing task without activity in the timed interval should produce a 'set' for timing using decay characteristics. If one group were to receive this kind of pretraining, would their performance differ in a second timing task with an interval in which activity occurred, from a group with no prior training or from a group which had experienced this type of input timing situation? Obviously a great deal of research is necessary before questions of this sort may be answered.

Other problems await investigation. What role, if any, does 'cognitive' timing play in the motor skill situation? A third strategy of timing may be available to subjects with greater merits in some situations. Counting or some other form of subvocal 'cognitive' behaviour may be used by some subjects in order to time responses. At least at the anecdotal level training often seems to take this form. (Do parachutists still count to 3 before pulling the rip-cord?) However, distinguishing between subjects who use sub-vocal counting techniques and those using some proprioceptive measure does not entirely clarify the issue. There is evidence dating back to Watson (1926) which suggests that muscular movements occur in the speech mechanisms when silent reading or any subvocal speech activity occurs. In other words, subvocal counting techniques may rely on proprioceptive factors. Aarons (1971) provided a further complication to this problem when he noted that although muscle activity frequently occurs in the laryngeal area during subvocalization it is not characteristic of all individuals.·

These confusions may be summarised in the following way. After learning, subjects may time responses without preview on the basis of either:—

1   decay of proprioceptive stimulation from previous responses;
2   proprioceptive input from previous responses; or
3   some cognitive measure such as subvocalized counting which may also provide proprioceptive information for some individuals.

Whether these problems of individual differences are soluble within the context of the current research strategies remains to be seen. A differential approach might be more in order at this stage. In terms of methodology it is also appropriate to mention the work of McConchie and Rutschmann (1970). They noted that in the timing of short intervals, differences exist between the use of reproductions, productions and verbal estimations of time. Comparisons across studies may therefore have limited value unless identical procedures were used.

7

PROPRIOCEPTION
AND
TRAINING

Chapter

7 PROPRIOCEPTION AND TRAININ

Introduction

Although an understanding of the principles of learning and those factors which influence the process is essential for the teacher, this kind of information does not have practical value in teaching unless it leads to predictions concerning the effectiveness of different teaching or training methods. The dichotomy between the study of learning and the study of training is quite well defined. In the field of psychology the application of learning principles to the problems of teaching has been remarkably small. There are notable exceptions, of course, e.g. the design of teaching machines which have evolved from Skinnerian approaches to learning. Nevertheless it remains true that a vast proportion of studies dealing with learning have been unconcerned with the techniques of training. Perhaps this has been due to unpreparedness on the part of psychologists to claim sufficient knowledge of learning principles for effective application to be made. To some extent it is a sound position: that while learning theory is still controversial little value may be derived from the application of theoretical concepts which may be invalidated by future research. This idealistic position is of little value, however, to the teacher or trainer who is either dissatisfied with current practices in teaching or wishes to maintain an improvement in his teaching effectiveness.

In an excellent foreword, Meredith (1965) has pointed out an additonal problem. 'In techniques of training, we find the experienced trainer often over-confident of the superiority of his particular methods—more by reason of his own facility in handling them than from any demonstrated comparison with alternative methods.' The trainer is in the unenviable position, therefore, of receiving both condemnation for maintaining his own teaching practices and either contradictory or an absence of advice on how to change them.

It is intended in this chapter to consider how the knowledge concerning proprioception has been applied in teaching and training methods. Both experimental and non-experimental views are considered. It is not intended

159

that advice should be given to the trainer for two distinct reasons. Firstly, where non-experimental material is criticized, it would not seem appropriate to offer alternatives without supporting empirical evidence. Secondly, any suggestion that experimental findings apply to a wider range of training situations may be misleading unless the experimental work is replicated in those situations. To quote Meredith (1965) once more, '. . . An awareness of experimental findings must be paralleled by competence in analysing tasks in order to determine how and where any particular principles may reasonably be applied . . . The actual findings of an experiment may well vary from one group of subjects to another and from one set of physical equipment to another'. (Meredith, 1965, pp. xi).

Information Feedback

Frequent reference has been made to the concept of feedback in the discussion of proprioception. The term has been used in its servo-mechanistic sense indicating that the feedback is derived from activity produced by the subject. This feedback is intrinsic to the activity. Subjects may, however, receive information from the experimenter over which the subject has no control. Traditionally, although not exclusively, this information has been given verbally by the experimenter, but there is no reason why this external information cannot be given through any modality.

In order to avoid any confusion the term 'information feedback' is used here according to the definition by Bilodeau (1966). She pointed out that information feedback is essentially the same as the concept 'knowledge of results' but '. . . Knowledge of results refers to the subject's awareness of the effects of his responses, some other term is needed for the variables that in turn control the subject's awareness and evaluations'. The term 'information feedback' therefore is used here to refer to stimuli under the experimenter's control, and related to a response and presented during the course of a response or at the end. (A paraphrase of Bilodeau, 1966, pp. 256).

In the learning of any task an experimenter may provide various forms of information feedback, the categories of which have been listed by Holding, (1965). He suggested that the information may be concurrent or terminal, i.e. information may be given at the end of the task or trial, or during its execution. Should the information be presented terminally, it may follow immediately upon the termination of the response or be delayed for a period of time. The information may also be given at the end of each individual response or accumulated over a series of responses and finally may be presented either verbally or non-verbally.

With this introduction in mind it is possible to examine the evidence which has been gathered concerning information feedback and proprioception.If a subject is told that a previous response is correct, presumably he is able to identify the proprioceptive feedback with which that response was associated. Over a number of trials, therefore, the subject should learn what a correct response 'feels' like. Adams (1971) in his closed loop theory of motor learning regarded this response to information as an essential although transient phase, after which the subject may monitor his own performance. Obviously in most real-life situations a learner will not necessarily need the information feedback since that level of information may be available by simple observation of his response. It is easy to forget, therefore, that this knowledge is of critical importance for the acquisition of skill.

It is easier to realise that more detailed information should enhance learning. At the empirical level this hypothetical interpretation may be tested in the following way. By blindfolding subjects so that accuracy of responding may not be observed, different qualities of information may be provided to the subject. It would be predicted that the greater the detail of information provided by the experimenter, the more accurately the subject should identify the correct proprioceptive feedback and the better the performance should be. In fact this paradigm formed one of the first series of experiments on information feedback. Thorndike (1927) used a line drawing task in which subjects without visual information were required to produce lines of 3, 4, 5 or 6 inches in length. Under the 'no information' feedback condition Thorndike found that not only was there no improvement in subjects' performance but that accuracy actually deteriorated in the course of the experiment. In a second blindfold condition subjects were merely told whether they had made a correct or an incorrect response. (A correct response was arbitrarily defined as a line which was within a quarter inch of the desired goal). This group showed marked improvement over trials. The experiment provided support for the hypothesis that information feedback improves performance and may be interpreted as supporting the position that information concerning the proprioceptive feedback associated with a correct response enabled subjects to identify and learn the qualities of that feedback, so that they could be reproduced on subsequent trials. In a replication of the Thorndike (1927) experiment, Trowbridge and Cason (1932) used four different conditions, a control, nonsense syllables as information feedback, correct/incorrect given as information feedback and a condition in which a group was given a more detailed analysis in which distance from the desired target was provided. High error scores were found in both control and nonsense syllable conditions, with a significant improvement consequent upon correct/incorrect information and best of all, by a wide margin, the group which had received detailed information feedback. In terms of the above hypothesis detailed information had enabled even more exact identification of the correct proprioceptive feedback. In a further analysis of the problem, Seashore and Bavelas (1941) contended that it was possible to detect learning in the group which had no information feedback. This group, although producing great absolute errors and no improvement with trials, did in fact decrease in the variability of their responses. It may be hypothesized that in this case subjects were matching proprioceptive feedback, not with some external reference point provided by the experimenter, but with the memory of the proprioceptive stimulation from a preceding response. That is, subjects became more consistent in their responding as they attempted to replicate a previous movement.

Although these experiments lend support to the prediction that information feedback enables accurate determination of correct proprioceptive stimulation, an alternative explanation of the results is possible. If responding is pre-programmed, i.e. under motor rather than proprioceptive feedback control, then the information feedback from the experimenter may provide subjects with an understanding of the correct value of muscle impetus or force to apply. Subjects should therefore improve in their performance as a function of increased accuracy in the preprogrammed motor response. At the present time it is not possible to choose between these alternative explanations. The crucial experiment would be the replication of Trowbridge and Cason's (1932) study using an additional group whose proprioceptive cues are blocked by an anaesthetic. If there is no reduction in level of performance by the information feedback groups under this condition it would support the motor programming hypothesis. However, the view expressed concerning the learned relationship between proprioceptive and information feedback may be considered the more parsimonious explanation for the following reason. Learning involving other modalities, e.g. vision or audition, shows similar effects of providing information feedback. Thus, in concept learning and verbal learning it is the perceptual characteristics of stimuli associated with a response labelled 'correct' through information feedback, which are learned. This may be simply stated using an example. Where subjects are required to visually discriminate between stimuli, information feedback improves performance. It may be assumed that this effect is due to subjects learning which stimulus has been designated as correct and which incorrect. The perceptual characteristics of the stimuli therefore become linked with the information feedback. In a motor skill situation the same argument may apply in that subjects improve in performance because of an identification of the correct proprioceptive stimuli on the basis of information feedback. Until the crucial experiment is performed this explanation may be preferred on the grounds of parsimony. It is also possible that both motor programming and proprioceptive feedback are involved. Initial, large movements may be made on the basis of motor programming and fine terminal adjustments result from proprioceptive feedback. This inference may be made from the work of Baker and Young (1960) who suggested improvement in performance with the presentation of information feedback occurred in two discrete stages. In the first stage approximate gross movements are made, and in the second the finer adjustments are achieved. They demonstrated that with the removal of information feedback the fine adjustments deteriorate more rapidly than the gross movements, indicating the possibility that different processes are involved.

Unfortunately the area of information feedback is plagued with experimental difficulties in the identification of the properties of this kind of feedback. Bilodeau (1966) distinguished between empirical and theoretical properties. In her analysis the empirical properties of information feedback include response strengthening, the sustaining of performance and the elimination of previously established responses. On the other hand, theoretically the properties may be regarded as either directive, motivating or reinforcing. She pointed out that information feedback may fulfill one or more of these functions. Explanations of the effects of information feedback in terms of only one function tend to be confounded. However, experimentally it is difficult to provide only one form of information feedback. In other words, single statements of information to the subject may be directive, motivating *and* reinforcing.

To recapitulate; giving information feedback, it is assumed, enables subjects to identify proprioceptive feedback associated with correct responding. The precise way in which the feedback operates has not been identified because of confounding variables and because it is not known to what extent motor programming may be involved. Generally speaking the greater the detail of information given, the better the level of performance. There are, however, limits to the degree to which subjects can make use of information feedback. Obviously, where information is provided in a line drawing experiment for example, in units which are smaller than the difference threshold, no advantage would be gained over the use of units which are at the difference threshold. Holding (1965) also noted that highly precise information feedback may be disruptive of later performance. If the objective of providing information feedback during learning is to facilitate the acquisition of a response which may then be produced in the absence of information feedback, then highly detailed information may not be optimum. In a line drawing task, Holding and Macrae (1964) demonstrated that over-precise information feedback during training may act as a 'crutch' and after its removal performance may significantly deteriorate.

This effect is illustrated in an experiment by Annett (1959). Subjects learned to exert a given level of pressure on a plunger. One group received verbal information feedback and the other received visual information in the form of a moving spot on an oscilloscope which centred on a target when the correct pressure was applied. A third group also received visual information, but this was provided by having the subject view his response on the oscilloscope after the response was completed. After the initial training, information feedback was removed for all groups and significantly poorer performances were found for the group which had received the continuous detailed information from the oscilloscope. The obvious inference from these results is that the proprioceptive feedback coincident with accurate responding had to be remembered in both conditions in which information was presented terminally. In the concurrent condition, which provided highly detailed information, there was no need for subjects to remember the proprioceptive feedback associated with correct responding. More will be said concerning memory for proprioceptive feedback and information feedback at a later stage.

It appears therefore that information feedback is preferable to no information feedback and that some detail is preferable to correct/incorrect information, but that the effect of precision in information will depend on the task and upon whether subsequent performance in the absence of information feedback is the goal of the training.

Most experiments have shown some reduction in level of performance after withdrawal of information feedback. Dees and Grindley (1951) observed that deterioration of performance was largely due to overshooting. A similar observation was made by Dyal (1966) except that tendency to overshoot after removal of information feedback was only found in subjects who had a tendency to undershoot prior to being given information feedback. The inference according to Welford (1968) is that information feedback '. . . produces a general tendency to overcorrect initial biases and that this in turn is modified and held in check by the detailed knowledge given trial by trial'.

The influence of memory on information feedback has been investigated in some detail. There are two sources of forgetting which may influence the effectiveness of the information feedback. Firstly, there is the interval between the end of a response and the presentation of the information. Sufficient memory of the proprioceptive feedback must be retained for the subject to relate the information and the feedback from that response. Secondly, retention of this relationship must occur in order for it to have an effect upon the subsequent response. The different types of delay of information feedback have been diagrammed by Holding (1965), (see Fig. 22). This simplification illustrates the different ways in which the effects of information feedback may be influenced by temporal factors. The results of experiments which relate information feedback to proprioceptive cues have not however provided a clear-cut answer to the effects of delay. The reasons for the contradictory evidence are also unclear but certain speculations may be made based on two distinct factors. Firstly, in experimental terms, evidence derived in different task situations may be the result of different levels of proprioceptive feedback. In other words, proprioceptive stimulation

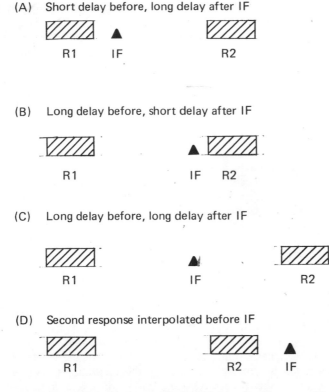

Fig. 22. The locus of information feedback. R1 is a first response; R2 is a second response; IF is the information feedback from RI. (Reprinted with permission from D. H. Holding, Principles of Training, 1965. Pergamon Press, Ltd.)

varies from task to task and therefore differences are likely to exist in the degree to which this stimulation may be retained. Similarly, the way in which information is given by the experimenter varies and the success with which the two kinds of feedback—information and proprioceptive—are integrated by the subject may also vary. There may also be subject preferences in terms of modalities through which information is derived. All these factors may influence the degree to which delay can be tolerated.

At a more theoretical level it will be remembered that Bilodeau (1966) pointed out that information feedback may have reinforcing and motivating properties as well as being directive. It is highly likely that delay of information feedback will have a different effect upon these properties. For example, reinforcing stimuli decrease in effectiveness as controllers of behaviour with increasing delay. The degree to which information feedback fulfills either of these roles may determine the degree to which delay influences the learning process.

Evidence for delay between the end of the response and the information feedback illustrates the contradictory nature of the evidence, (see category B of Fig. 22). Delays of up to 30 seconds were shown by Denny Allard, Hall and Rokeach (1960) and Dyal (1964) to have significant detrimental effects on the acquisition process. Bilodeau and Bilodeau (1958) also showed large effects on the delay of information feedback for an hour. However, Bilodeau and Bilodeau were unable to demonstrate any effect of delay for periods of 30 seconds. Dyal, Wilson and Berry (1965) provided a solution to this contradiction. They interpreted the results of the foregoing studies as a measurement artifact and demonstrated that as the technique of measuring accuracy of response was changed, completely different effects of delay were found. A reduction in level of performance with delay was noted if the proportion of scores falling within an arbitrary correct zone was used as the method of measurement, whereas no influence of delay was demonstrated if the actual error scores were measured. Welford (1968) inferred that delay of information feedback results in little effect on mean accuracy, but causes more relatively large deviations. The problem, however, is by no means entirely solved, since Becker, Mussina and Persons (1963) produced evidence directly contradictory of the Dyal, Wilson and Berry (1965) study.

In the case of information feedback which is given immediately and followed by different time intervals (category A in Fig. 22) there is somewhat less evidence. However, it could be predicted that more deleterious results of delay would be found in this case because of the greater memory load involved. That is, in delay before giving information subjects must retain some memory of the proprioceptive stimulation for comparison with information. However, where delay occurs between information and the next response subjects have to retain both the knowledge and the memory of the stimulation from the previous response and the relationship between the two. The evidence generally seems to support this prediction (Bilodeau and Bilodeau, 1958). Unfortunately many of the studies in this area have produced confounded results. Bilodeau (1966) pointed out that studies in which the inter-trial interval remains constant and information feedback is given at different points during the interval should be more properly called studies on the locus of information feedback rather than studies of the delay of information feedback, since changes of one kind of delay automatically change the other, (compare A and B on Fig. 22). Similarly, if one form of delay (e.g. interval between end of first response and information feedback) is constant and the other is varied, then inter-trial interval must change, (compare B and C on Fig. 22). The result is that the two learning situations are no longer identical. The effects of temporal variables are therefore by no means clear as yet and the 'teaching machine propaganda' (as Bilodeau, 1966, called it) which suggests deleterious effects of delay may have overstated its importance.

A final problem in terms of delay consists of the activity which occurs during the interval between the response and the information (line D in Fig. 22). In studies on information feedback this problem has been investigated by having subjects produce an interpolated response between a first response and the information for that first response. This has been called a trials delay of information feedback. Lorge and Thorndike (1935) showed improvement with a six-seconds delay of information feedback, but not when an interpolated trial was given in the interval. This would be predicted on the basis of interference in memory of the proprioceptive stimulation from the second trial on the stimulation from the first. However, Bilodeau (1956) was able to demonstrate some learning with trials delay, but found increasingly detrimental effects with increasing numbers of interpolated trials.

In the course of the discussion of information feedback it has been emphasized that information may be provided in any modality to the subject. Some comparison of the effects of using different modalities was made in studies by Lincoln (1956). He considered that since the objective of information feedback is to give subjects knowledge of the relationship between the proprioceptive stimulation derived from responding and how far that response deviated from the one desired, it should be possible for the information to be fed back to the subject in proprioceptive terms. In other words, after a subject has completed a response it should be possible to provide him with proprioceptive error information. Lincoln (1956) approached the problem in the following manner. Subjects were required to learn to turn a handwheel at a rate of 100 rpm. Three groups were used, each of which had 30 x 15 second trials. One of these groups received verbal information feedback concerning their average rate error in the preceding trial. A second group received proprioceptive error information. During the inter-trial interval these subjects grasped a handwheel while the handwheel was motor driven at a rate equivalent to their average rate error on the previous trial. They were also told whether this was a positive or negative error, but were given no other verbal information. A third group did not receive any error information of a verbal nature. After each learning trial the handwheel was grasped by the subject and motor driven at the standard rate of 100 rpm. The results of the experiment indicated that rapid learning of the desired rate occurred for all three groups. In order of superiority, after the learning trials, were the verbal error group, the proprioceptive error group and the proprioceptive standard group. The difference between the groups was significant. After training was completed information feedback was removed for all groups. One third of each group attempted this task immediately, a second third was tested after a one hour retention interval and the remaining third was tested one day later. Length of retention interval was not found to influence the accuracy of performing the task in the absence of information feedback and little loss in accuracy was noted for all groups over the level of performance at the end of the learning period. In terms of groups, no significant differences were found between the proprioceptive error and the verbal error information groups and both were significantly superior to the proprioceptive standard group.

The results of this experiment are surprising in some ways. Perhaps the relatively poor performance of the proprioceptive standard group is easiest to explain. The proprioceptive feedback derived in the learning trials was produced through active muscular activity, whereas in the information feedback process the proprioceptive feedback was produced on the basis of passively experienced movement. The fact that subjects were less able to use this entirely different information is not too surprising. However, this does not explain why the proprioceptive error information group should have been superior. Perhaps the additonal verbal information (positive or negative) which they received accounted for the difference. A control group which received the verbal information—too fast or too slow only (without any error information)—would have indicated to what extent the relative superiority of the proprioceptive error information group was due to the verbal information they received. The superiority of the error group also indicates a further principle of information feedback. Welford (1968) pointed out that '. . . information given should indicate the discrepancy between what is required and what has been achieved rather than merely give a reminder of requirement or some broad measure of achievement'. (Welford, 1968, pp. 305).

Guidance and Proprioception

Lincoln's (1956) study bridges a gap between two concepts involved in training. Information feedback and guidance are related terms and it is relatively easy to confuse them. The distinction between the two has been described by Annett (1959) as a difference between giving knowledge after a response (information feedback), and giving knowledge before a response (guidance). In this sense the proprioceptive standard group was given both information feedback and guidance. Normally, however, experiments in guidance involve pretraining in responding in which the experimenter manipulates the subject's activity so that he is always correct. Test trials without guidance are then used to demonstrate the efficacy of this technique over learning without guidance.

In terms of learning efficiency the rationale for this procedure may be described in the following way. Early learning is characterized by large errors in performance and these are gradually eliminated as learning progresses.

However, subjects may learn errors as well as learning the correct responses which slows down the acquisition process. It is assumed that an active response made early in learning is retained better than the correction which may be given verbally as information feedback and not actively produced by the subject. When the situation re-occurs there will be a tendency for that incorrect response to be repeated rather than its correction. Essentially this argument is based on a contiguity S-R view of learning in which temporal association of stimuli and responses is the important factor and reinforcement (information feedback) is reduced to a minor role. This view has found empirical support in the work of Kay (1951) who demonstrated that older subjects in particular have difficulty in eliminating errors made during the early part of the learning process. It will be noted that the principles outlined above also form part of the basis of teaching machines.

In a motor skill context, this rationale has implications in terms of proprioceptive stimulation. Experience of proprioceptive stimulation associated with a correct response should enable the replication of movements to be made more accurately on subsequent trials. This assumption does not apply to all types of guidance situations. It was pointed out in the study by Lincoln (1956) that if the subject is guided passively through a movement the proprioceptive stimulation is likely to be very different from that produced in appropriately responding without guidance simply as a function of active versus passive movement. This discrepancy in the proprioceptive feedback provided under pre-training and learning conditions may account for the highly divergent results which have been found in the application of guidance to motor skill learning. However, even in the proprioceptive standard situation of the Lincoln experiment, learning did occur, indicating that perhaps subjects are capable of translating passively experienced movement into its active counterpart, but that this may not be an optimum training procedure.

The distinction between the effects of active and passive training is not restricted to the qualities of proprioceptive feedback. For example, Von Wright (1957) had three groups of subjects learn an identical maze. The control group practised on this maze until a criterion performance had been achieved. A second group received four pre-training guided trials in which they simply followed the correct path through the maze. Their movements were restricted to the correct path. A third group were given four pre-training trails in which they had preview of the correct route to follow at all the choice points of the maze. On arrival at a choice point subjects in this group could see which route was blocked and which was the correct route. After the fourth trial all groups used the same maze in which incorrect choices could not be previewed. The results of the experiment indicated superiority in learning for the two guidance groups. The group which had made no errors but had actively chosen one course over another at choice points with preview were greatly superior to the group who had followed the true path without choice points. These results may be interpreted as supporting active cognitive responding over passive cognitive responding and do not reflect differences between active and passive proprioceptive feedback since both guided groups were active.

Perhaps more relevant to the subject of active versus passive proprioceptive feedback is the series of studies by Holding and Macrae. (Holding and Macrae, 1964; Macrae and Holding, 1965; Holding and Macrae, 1966). Holding and Macrae (1964) required blindfolded subjects to learn an arm movement of four inches, involving pushing a slider along a rod. Pretraining of various forms was given to different groups of subjects. One group experienced the movement passively whereas another group received both passive guidance and interpolated trials without guidance. A final group actively moved the slider over the required distance in pretraining, the slider being blocked after four inches. It would be predicted on the basis of the similarities of proprioceptive feedback that those training trials in which active movement was experienced would be superior to those in which passive movement occurred. Holding and Macrae's (1964) results supported this hypothesis. The difference between the groups with passive movement and those with alternating passive and active movement was minimal, however. Highly superior results were achieved by the active group.

In the same experiment, Holding and Macrae evaluated the relative advantages of guidance over information feedback. Two further groups were used each of which performed the training trials actively. One of these received correct/incorrect information and the other details of size and direction of error. The results showed that detailed information feedback produced better performance than correct/incorrect information. Of greater interest is the fact that the results of these two groups were both intermediate between the performance of the passive movement groups on the one hand, and the active movement groups on the other (see Fig. 23). In relative terms, the best performance was found with active practice in which subjects practised the experimental task, but whose movements were restricted to those that were correct. Slightly less advantageous training was found by giving information feedback associated with active movement. Inferior performance was achieved when passive movement or alternate passive trials were given as training. It should be noted that all groups improved relative to a control group which had no prior training. The degree to which the relative value of these different forms of training is generalizable to other skill situations is debatable. Presumably, optimal training techniques are highly task-specific.

Further experiments by Holding and Macrae (1966) and by Macrae and Holding (1965) amplified these results showing that some guidance on slightly different tasks may also be effective in training and that partial response forcing also produces gains in performance.

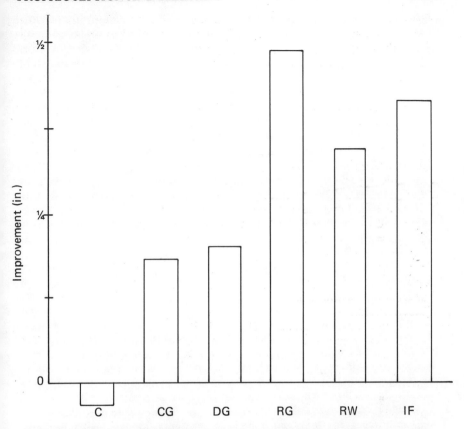

Fig. 23. A comparison of information feedback with various forms of guidance. Group C was a control group; Group CG had forced-response guidance throughout; Group DG had forced-response guidance on alternate trials; Group RG had guidance by restriction; Group RW had right-wrong information; Group IF had full information feedback (After Holding and Macrae, 1964, Ergonomics, 7, 289-295. Reprinted with permission).

Whiting (1969) has pointed out that in the skill training situation outside the laboratory the efficiency of guidance may be limited by the accuracy with which the trainer can identify the exact movement required.

Part versus Whole Learning

In complex skills a decision must frequently be made by the experimenter or trainer whether the skill should be taught as a whole with repetition of the total task until success is achieved or whether the skill should be broken into parts to be practised separately until they may be joined together to form the complete task. There has been a considerable amount of research concerning the optimum kind of training procedure. The results of the research have been disappointing however, and no firm conclusions have been reached. This has been the case in fine motor skills, gross motor skills and in verbal learning. In the latter case experimental evidence has been so inconclusive that it led Postman and Goggin (1966) to propose an invariance hypothesis. Their suggestion was that procedural variations in learning have little effect on the speed of learning and total time spent in learning is the crucial factor irrespective of the way in which this time is divided.

In motor learning the evidence is equally contradictory. Knapp (1963) and Holding (1965) have both provided excellent reviews of the field from different points of view. The disparity between the various sets of evidence appears to be the result of the wide range of skills on which tests have been made and also, as Knapp (1963) noted, the poor quality of some of the research in the field.

In terms of proprioceptive stimulation it would be predicted that the whole method of training should always prove superior. If proprioception serves any function in the timing of motor responses as suggested in Chapter Six, it is obvious that superior timing of components in the total response pattern may be better learned where the skill is practised in total. Also, if Adams' (1971) closed loop theory of motor learning is correct, then the development of a perceptual trace or memory for proprioceptive feedback against which incoming stimuli may be compared, is certain to be enhanced by repeated 'whole' trials. Such a perceptual trace would be presumably more liable to interference where the skill was practised in component parts.

Other factors would also tend to make the whole method optimum. If a skill requires a rhythmic sequence of movements for example, superiority would be predicted. Similarly, if the sub-components of the task need to be put together in a way which is not immediately compatible to the learner, the time spent in so doing may be disproportionate. Holding (1965) cited the example of learning breast-stroke swimming in which arm and leg movements may be practised separately. Here the rhythmic nature of the task, in addition to the fact that the combination of the two sets of movements may not be entirely obvious initially, cause the whole method of learning to be preferable.

The fact that part methods have sometimes been found optimum and sometimes no difference between the methods has been reported indicates that counterbalancing factors must be present. Notable amongst these is the complexity of the task. Many motor skills are simply too difficult for the subjects to acquire as a whole and in this case sub-division is likely to result in superior learning. In terms of the present discussion the advantages gained from the learning of a proprioceptive feedback sequence are more than off-set by the simplification which occurs in the sub-division of a highly complex task. Alternatively there may be skills in which the sub-components of the task are highly independent. The acquisition of these tasks may not suffer through compartmentalising the training (Naylor and Briggs, 1963). In part this may result because the proprioceptive feedback associated with each correct component may also be learned as independent units.

Whilst the evidence remains contradictory in motor learning, it is unlikely that the invariance hypothesis is tenable as it appears to be in verbal learning. Motor tasks have a coherence not found in experimental verbal material, which predicts superiority for whole learning methods. The ambiguity of experimental results may be due to invariance in procedural effects in verbal learning, but appears rather to be the result of competing forces which vary in strength depending upon the task in the motor learning context.

Occlusion techniques of training.

If subjects perform tasks better by attending to relevant cues, and if there exist relevant proprioceptive cues, it would seem probable that one function of training should be the indication of these relevant cues to the learner. Unfortunately there exists no language in which the trainer may describe those proprioceptive cues which are relevant. One technique has been used infrequently in order to compel subjects to attend to proprioceptive information. Subjects are required at some stage during training to perform the skill in the absence of visual cues. The rationale for this procedure is simply that during the learning of a particular task subjects may be attending to visual cues to the exclusion of those derived from proprioceptors. It is therefore hypothesized that when subjects are forced into a training procedure in which only proprioceptive cues are available, they become aware of proprioceptive information and identify relevant cues of this nature. This, in turn, facilitates performance when visual information is re-presented in the learning trials proper. The evidence for this position is based upon two underlying assumptions. Firstly, that without training subjects attend more closely to visual information. The evidence for this has been documented in Chapter Four. Secondly, it is assumed that there are relevant proprioceptive cues which may be used in the control of skill. This is demonstrated by the fact that visual attention is released during later stages of practice and a skill may come under proprioceptive control anyway. (The material concerning this hypothesis is reviewed in Chapter Five.) The evidence concerning the use of occlusion techniques in facilitating the learning process may therefore be examined on the understanding that there are good grounds for the validity of the underlying assumptions.

Evidence has been produced by Ragsdale (1950) which demonstrated that in teaching a golf drive subjects performed better if some practice were given in the absence of visual cues. A later study by Espenschade (1958) provided some partly contradictory evidence. In her experiment, subjects were required during training to throw small sand-bags at a target from a distance of twelve feet. One group was blindfolded for initial practice. It was found that subjects with this form of training could increase their level of performance in terms of distance thrown, but accuracy in hitting the target did not improve significantly.

It is perhaps surprising that both these studies should have used skills which are essentially ballistic. Whiting (1969) pointed out that experiments on the golf swing have confirmed its ballistic nature. It was noted in Chapter Four that the relevance of proprioceptive feedback in the case of ballistic skills is likely to be small. It is perfectly possible that the improvement noted by Espenschade (1958) therefore was due to information feedback identifying the correct motor aspect of performance rather than the proprioceptive feedback associated with a correct response. This may partially explain why distance scores improved but accuracy did not.

So far as the author is aware, formal tests of the hypothesis in non-ballistic skills have not been made with occlusion used as training for fully sighted performance. There is, however, indirect evidence from the training of the partially sighted that occlusion has value as a training procedure. Cohen (1966) noted that '... the partially sighted person may rely more heavily on his other senses (rather than inadequate vision) if he is blindfolded during training'. This suggestion was independently taken up by Dickinson (1968a). In his study, methods of training those with residual vision in a balancing task were investigated. It has been demonstrated (Leonard, 1966) that blind people are inferior in balance ability compared with those who are sighted. Leonard also noted that the blind with some residual vision are no better at balancing than those totally blind. Dickinson (1968a) contended that the reason for this situation was perhaps that those with residual vision were relying too heavily on inadequate visual information. In the laboratory situation this hypothesis was tested by having subjects attempt a mobile balancing task under two visual conditions. In one of these a single minimal visual stimulus was provided in an otherwise dark environment. Subjects were required to learn to balance in this situation. Some subjects practised under this condition continuously whereas others completed part of the training trials under blindfold conditions. It was found that training trials using occlusion did produce a significant effect upon performance in the test trials using the minimal visual cue. Training trials were divided in half and it was found that giving blindfold practice in the second half of the training trials produced superior performances compared with a group which practised with blindfold trials in the first half and a group which practised with all trials blindfold. The benefit of interpolated blindfold trials, Dickinson (1968) assumed, derived from less than theoretical reasons. He contended that the subjects needed to become familiar with the task before experiencing training with occlusion. The results supported the hypothesis that the use of occlusion may facilitate performance. The suggestion was made that in the condition where visual information is available but is inadequate for the balancing task, subjects will rely on this information. If their attention is directed to proprioceptive stimuli, learning to use these enables superior performance when the additional visual information is available. When this method of training was subsequently attempted with blind children who had residual vision, it was found that although very small sample sizes were used, similar results were achieved (Dickinson 1968b).

Tentatively it may be assumed that occlusion is of value in the direction of attention to proprioceptive stimuli. However, further experimental work must be undertaken in order to demonstrate whether the phenomenon has generality. Also, it is necessary to point out that the simple process of occlusion may not serve to identify for the learner the cues which are relevant, but merely provide a stimulus array to which subjects may not otherwise attend. Perhaps the saliency of relevant proprioceptive cues within any task will determine the efficacy of this type of training.

Non-experimental Views

The medium of physical activity has been used in part as an educative method for some years. The growth of modern educational gymnastics, particularly in Britain, has emphasized the fact that physical activity in the school should and can educate as well as train. The controversies which surround this attitude fall outside the scope of this book. However, Whiting (1969) has pointed out that educative and training principles do not necessarily coincide. 'It is this two-fold approach training in ball games and education through the medium of ball games—that bedevils the methodology of instruction.' (Whiting, 1969, pp. viii). The same principle applies in the context of proprioception. The relationship between proprioception and training has been discussed thus far with reference to experimental evidence of training variables in the laboratory. There have also been claims made for the training of proprioceptive sensitivity by those involved in education through movement (Morison, 1969, and Randall, 1961, for example).

It should be appreciated that these objectives related to proprioception are only a small part of the total of movement education's point of view. Criticism of these objectives does not imply criticism of other aspects (see Locke, 1969). Views with respect to proprioception can be summarised in the following way. If a child is exposed to a large number of movement experiences then he will become familiar with various forms of proprioceptive feedback. This will enable the child to understand the characteristics of personal movement and thereby facilitate future skill acquisition. In the light of existing evidence, two points emerge from this view. Firstly, although it is undeniable that the accurate utilization of proprioceptive feedback relies on experience and learning, the evidence appears to warrant the assumption that the learning is specific. Secondly, it is possible that two quite distinct processes may be involved. Dickinson (1970) commented that general movement training may give either increased sensitivity to proprioceptive cues, but may also serve to indicate to the performer relevant rather than irrelevant supra-threshold proprioceptive cues. Optimal training experience may be different depending on the degree to which these components contribute to any facilitation of future skill acquisition. Without the empirical evidence, this discussion is essentially speculative. However, the issue is raised at this point since it outlines a field of research which is ripe for empirical study.

REFERENCES

REFERENCES

Addenda to Bibliography

AARONS, L. (1971). Subvocalization: Aural and E.M.G. feedback in reading. *Perceptual and Motor Skills,* **33,** 271-306.

ADAMS, J.A. (1968). Response feedback and learning. *Psychological Bulletin,* **70,** 486-504.

ADAMS, J.A. (1971). A closed-loop theory of motor learning. *Journal of Motor Behaviour,* **3,** 111-149.

ADAMS, J.A. & CREAMER, L.R. (1962). Proprioception variables as determiners of anticipatory timing behavior. *Human Factors,* **4,** 217-222.

ADAMS, J.A. & CREAMER, L.R. (1962). Anticipatory timing of continuous and discrete responses. *Journal of Experimental Psychology,* **63,** 84-90.

ADAMS, J.A. & DIJKSTRA, S. (1966). Short term memory for motor responses. *Journal of Experimental Psychology,* **71,** 314-318.

ADAMS, J.S. & XHIGNESSE, L.V. (1960). Some determinants of two-dimensional visual tracking behavior. *Journal of Experimental Psychology,* **60,** 391-403.

ADRIAN, E.D. (1926). The impulses produced by sensory nerve-endings. Part 1. *Journal of Psysiology,* **61,** 49-72.

ADRIAN, E.D., CATTELL, M. & HOAGLAND, H. (1931). Sensory discharges in single cutaneous nerve fibres. *Journal of Physiology,* **72,** 377-392.

ADRIAN, E.D. & ZOTTERMAN, Y. (1926). The impulses produced by sensory nerve-endings. Part 2. The response of a single end-organ. *Journal of Physiology,* **61,** 151-171.

ALLUISI, E.A. (1966). Attention and vigilance as mechanisms of response: comments on Professor Adams' Paper. In E.A. Bildeau (Ed.), *Acquisition of Skill.* New York: Academic Press.

ALVARES, K.M. & HULIN, C.L. (1972). Two explanations of temporal changes in ability-skill relationships: A literature review and theoretical analysis. *Human Factors,* **14,** 295-308.

ANNETT, J. (1959). Learning a pressure under conditions of immediate and delayed knowledge of results. *Quarterly Journal of Experimental Psychology,* **11,** 3-15.

ARMSTRONG, H.G. (1943). *Principles and Practice of Aviation Medicine. (2nd Edition).* Baltimore: Williams and Wilkins.

ATKINSON, R.C. & SHIFFRIN, R.M. (1968). Human memory: a proposed system and its control processes. In K.W. Spence & J.T. Spence, (Eds.) "The psychology of Learning and Motivation: Advances in research and theory, Vol. 2. New York: Academic Press.

ATTNEAVE, F. (1959). *Applications of Information Theory to Psychology.* New York: Holt.

ATTNEAVE, F. (1966). Cybernetic theory and analysis of learning, comments on Professor Smith's paper. In E.A. Bilodeau, (Ed.) *Acquisition of skill.* New York: Academic Press.

BACHMAN, J.C. (1961). Motor learning and performance as related to age and sex in two measures of balance coordination. *Research Quarterly,* **32,** 123-137.

BAHRICK, H.P. 1957. An analysis of the stimulus variables influencing the proprioceptive control of movement. *Psychological Review,* **64,** 324-328.

BAHRICK, H.P., BENNETT, W.F. & FITTS, P.M. (1955). Accuracy of positioning responses as a function of spring loading in a control. *Journal of Experimental Psychology,* **49,** 437-446.

BAHRICK, H.P., FITTS, P.M. & SCHNEIDER, R. (1955). The reproduction of simple movements as a function of proprioceptive feedback. *Journal of Experimental Psychology,* **49,** 445-454.

BAHRICK, H.P., NOBLE, M.E. & FITTS, P.M. (1954). Extra task performance as a measure of learning a primary task. *Journal of Experimental Psychology,* **48,** 292-302.

BAKAN, P. & WEILER, E. (1963). Kinesthetic after-effect and mode of exposure to inspection stimulus. *Journal of Experimental Psychology,* **65,** 319-320.

BARKER, C.H. & YOUNG, P. (1960). Feedback during training and retention of motor skills. *Canadian Journal of Psychology,* **14,** 257-264.

BARKER, D. (1948). The innervation of the muscle spindles. *Quarterly Journal of Microscopical Science,* **89,** 143-186.

BAKER, D. (1962). *Symposium on muscle receptors.* Hong Kong: Hong Kong University Press.

BASS, R.I. (1939). An analysis of the components of tests of semi-circular canal function and of static and dynamic balance. *Research Quarterly,* **10,** 35-52.

BATTIG, W.F. (1966). Facilitation and interference. In E.A. Bilodeau (Ed.) *Acquisition of Skill.* New York: Academic Press.

BECKER, P.W., MUSSINA, C.M. & PERSONS, R.W. (1963). Intertrial interval, delay of knowledge of results and motor performance. *Perceptual and Motor Skills,* 17, 559-563.
BEGBIE, G.H. (1966). The effects of alcohol and of varying amounts of visual information on a balancing test. *Ergonomics,* 9, 325-333.
BELL, C. (1942). On the nervous circle which connects the voluntary muscles with the brain. Cited in E.G. Boring.
BERRY, C.M., KARL, R.C. & HINSEY, J.C. (1950). Course of spinothalamic and medial lemniscus pathways in cat and rhesus monkey. *Journal of Neurophysiology,* 13, 149-156.
BILODEAU, E.A. (1966). Retention. In E.A. Bilodeau (Ed.) *Acquisition of Skill.* New York: Academic Press.
BILODEAU, E.A. & BILODEAU, I. McD. (1958). Variation of temporal intervals among critical events in five studies of knowledge of results. *Journal of Experimental Psychology,* 55, 603-612.
BILODEAU, I. McD. (1956). Accuracy of a simple positioning response with variation in the number of trials by which knowledge of results is delayed. *American Journal of Psychology,* 69, 434-437.
BILODEAU, I. McD. (1966). Information Feedback. In E.A. Bilodeau (Ed.) *Acquisition of Skill.* New York: Academic Press.
BLICK, K.A. & BILODEAU, E.A. (1963). Interpolated activity and the learning of a simple skill. *Journal of Experimental Psychology,* 65, 515-519.
BORING, E.G. (1942). *Sensation and Perception in the History of Experimental Psychology.* New York: Appleton-Century-Crofts.
BOSWELL, J.J. & BILODEAU, E.A. (1964). Short-term retention of a simple motor task as a function of interpolated activity. *Perceptual Motor Skills,* 18, 227-230.
BOURNE, L.E. & BEIR, E.G. (1961). Effect of duration of inspection upon kinesthetic figural after effects. *Journal of Genetic Psychology,* 65, 163-169.
BOYD, I.A. (1954). The histological structure of the receptors in the knee joint of the cat correlated with their physiological responses. *Journal of Physiology,* 124, 469-488.
BREININ, G.M. (1957). Electromyographic evidence for ocular proprioception in man. *Arch. Opthal.,* 57, 176-180.
BREUER, J. (1942). Uber die Funktion der Bogengänger der Ohrelabyrinthe. 1874. Cited in E.G. Boring.
BRINDLY, G.S. & MERTON, P.A. (1960). The absence of position sense in the human eye. *Journal of Physiology,* 153, 127-130.
BROADBENT, D.E. (1958). *Perception and Communication.* London: Pergamon Press.
BROWNE, K., LEE, L. & RING, P.A. (1954). Sensations of passive

182 PROPRIOCEPTIVE CONTROL OF HUMAN MOVEMENT

---

movement at the metatarso-phalangeal joint of the great toe in man. *Journal of Physiology,* **126,** 448-458.

BUGELSKI, B.R. (1956). *The Psychology of Learning.* New York: Holt, Rinehart and Winston.

BURKE, D. & Gibbs, C.B. (1965). A comparison of free moving and pressure levers in a positional and control system. *Ergonomics,* **8,** 23-29.

BURTT, H.E. (1918). The perception of slight changes of equilibrium with especial reference to problems of aviation. *Journal of Applied Psychology,* **2,** 101-115.

CALDWELL, L.S. (1956). The accuracy of constant angular displacement of the arm in the horizontal plane as influenced by the direction and locus of the primary adjustive movement. USA MRL Report, *Technical Report,* **233.**

CALDWELL, L.S. & HERBERT, M.J. (1956). The judgment of angular positions in the horizontal plane on the basis of kinesthetic cues. USA MRL Report, *Technical Report,* **216.**

CHARLES, J.P. & DUNCAN, C.P. (1959). The distance gradient in kinesthetic figural after effects. *Journal of Experimental Psychology,* **57,** 164-170.

CHERNIKOFF, R. & TAYLOR, F.V. (1952). Reaction time to kinesthetic stimulation resulting from sudden arm displacement. *Journal of Experimental Psychology,* **43,** 1-8.

CHRISTINA, R.W. (1970). Proprioception as a basis for the temporal anticipation of motor responses. *Journal of Motor Behaviour,* **2,** 125-133.

CLARK, B. & GRAYBIEL, A. (1949). Linear acceleration and deceleration as factors influencing non-visual orientation during flight. *Journal of Aviation Medicine,* **20,** 92-101.

CLARK, B. & GRAYBIEL, A. (1963). Perception of the postural vertical in normals and subjects with labyrinthine defects. *Journal of Experimental Psychology,* **65,** 490-494.

CLEGHORN, T.E. & DARCUS, H.D. (1952). The sensibility to passive movement of the human elbow joint. *Quarterly Journal of Experimental Psychology,* **4,** 66-77.

COCKERILL, I.M. (1972). The development of ballistic skill movements. In H.T.A. Whiting (Ed.), *Readings in Sports Psychology.* London: Henry Kimpton Publishers.

COHEN, J. (1966). The effects of blindness on children's development. *New Outlook for the Blind,* **60,** 150-154.

COOKSEY, F.S. (1946). Rehabilitation in vestibular injuries. *Proceedings of the Royal Society of Medicine,* **39,** 273-278.

COOPER, S. (1961). The responses of the primary and secondary endings of muscle spindles with intact motor innervation during applied stretch. *Quarterly Journal of Experimental Physiology,* **46,** 389-398.

CORAH, N. & COHEN, W. (1961). Attention and the kinesthetical figural after effect. *American Journal of Psychology,* **74**, 629-630.

CORSO, J.F. (1967). *The Experimental Psychology of Sensory Behaviour.* New York: Holt, Rinehart and Winston, Inc.

CRAIK, K.J.W. (1947). Theory of the human operator in control systems. I. The operator as an engineering system. *British Journal of Psychology,* **38**, 56-61.

CRAIK, K.J.W. (1948). Theory of the human operator in control systems. II. Man as an element in a control system. *British Journal of Psychology,* **38**, 142-148.

CRATTY, B.J. (1967). *Movement Behaviour and Motor Learning,* 2nd edition. London: Henry Kimpton.

CRATTY, B.J. & HUTTON, R.S. (1964). Figural after effects resulting from gross action patterns. *Research Quarterly,* **35**, 147-160.

CRON, G.W. & PRONKO, N.H. (1957). Development of the sense of balance in school children. *Journal of Educational Research,* **51**, 33-57.

CROSSMAN, E.R.F.W. (1959). A theory of the acquisition of speed-skill. *Ergonomics,* **2**, 153-166.

CRUM-BROWN, A. (1875). On the sense of rotation and the anatomy and physiology of the semicircular canals of the internal ear. *Journal of Anatomy,* **8**, 327-331.

DEES, V. & GRINDLEY, G.G. (1951). The effect of knowledge of results on learning and performance. The direction of the error in very simple skills. *Quarterly Journal of Experimental Psychology,* **3**, 36-42.

DEESE, J. & HULSE, S.H. (1967). *The Psychology of Learning,* 3rd edition. New York: McGraw-Hill Book Company.

DENNY, M.R, ALLARD, M., HALL, E. & ROKEACH, M. (1960). Supplementary report: Delay of knowledge of results, knowledge of task and intertrial interval. *Journal of Experimental Psychology,* **60**, 327.

DeOREO, K.D. & WADE, M.G. (1971). Dynamic and static balancing ability of preschool children. *Journal of Motor Behaviour,* **3**, 326-335.

DEUTSCH, J.A. & DEUTSCH, D. (1966). *Physiological Psychology.* Homewood, Illinois: The Dorsey Press.

DICKINSON, J. (1968a). The training of mobile balancing under a minimal visual cue situation. *Ergonomics,* **11**, 69-75.

DICKINSON, J. (1968b). *Studies in equilibrium and the role of vision.* Unpublished doctoral thesis, Nottingham University, England.

DICKINSON, J. (1969). The role of two factors in a gross motor aiming task. *British Journal of Psychology,* **60**, 465-470.

DICKINSON, J. (1970). A note on the concept of body awareness. *British Journal of Physical Education,* **1**, 34-36.

DICKINSON, J. (1972). Proprioceptive control of skilled behaviour. In H.T.A. Whiting (Ed.), *Readings in Sports Psychology.* London: Henry Kimpton Publishers.

DICKINSON, J. & LEONARD, J.A. (1967). The role of peripheral vision in static balancing. *Ergonomics,* **10,** 421-429.

DICKINSON, J. & RENNIE, A. (1970). Aiming skill in children; the importance of two factors during learning. *Carnegie Research Papers.*

DODGE, R. (1923). Thresholds of rotation. *Journal of Experimental Psychology,* **6,** 107-137.

DODWELL, P.C. (1970). *Visual pattern recognition.* New York. Holt, Rinehart and Winston, Inc.

DOW, R.S. (1942). The evolution and anatomy of the cerebellum. *Biology Review,* **17,** 179-220.

DYAL, J.A. (1966). Effects of delay of knowledge of results and subject response bias on extinction of a simple motor skill. *Journal of Experimental Psychology,* **71,** 559-563.

DYAL, J.A., WILSON, W.J. & BERRY, K.K. (1965). Acquisition and extinction of a simple motor skill as a function of delay of knowledge of results. *Quarterly Journal of Experimental Psychology,* **17,** 158-162.

ECCLES, J.C. (1967). Circuits in the cerebellar control of movement. *Proceedings of the National Academy of Sciences,* **58,** 336-343.

EDWARDS, A.S. (1946). Body sway and vision. *Journal of Experimental Psychology,* **36,** 526-535.

EDWARDS, A.S. (1947). Body sway and non-visual factors. *Journal of Psychology,* **23,** 241-254.

EKMAN, G. (1964). Is the power law a special case of Fechner's law? *Perceptual and Motor Skills,* **19,** 730.

ELDRED, E., GRANIT, R. & MERTON, P.A., (1953). Supraspinal control of the muscle spindles and its significance. *Journal of Physiology,* **122,** 498-523.

ELLIS, M.J. (1969). Control dynamics and timing a discrete motor response. *Journal of Motor Behaviour,* **1,** 119-134.

ELLIS, M.J., SCHMIDT, R.A. & WADE, M.G. (1968). Proprioception variables as determinants of lapsed-time estimation. *Ergonomics,* **11,** 577-586.

ENGEN, T. (1971). Psychophysics. In J.W. Kling and L.A. Riggs (Eds.) *Woodworth and Scholsberg's Experimental Psychology,* 3rd edition. New York: Holt, Rinehart and Winston, Inc.

ERLANGER, J. & GASSER, H.S. (1937). *Electrical signs of nervous activity.* Johnson Foundation Lectures. Philadel. University of Pennsylvania Press.

ESPENSCHADE, A. (1958). Kinesthetic awareness in motor learning. *Perceptual and Motor Skills,* **8,** 142.

ESPENSCHADE, A., DABLE, R.R. & SCHOENDAUBE, R. (1953). Dynamic balance in adolescent boys. *Research Quarterly,* **24,** 270-275.

ESTEP, D.P. (1957). Relationship of static equilibrium to ability in motor activities. *Research Quarterly,* **28,** 5-15.

ESTES, W.K. (1959). The statistical approach to learning theory. In S. Koch (Ed.), *Psychology: A Study of a Science*, Vol. 2. New York: McGraw-Hill.

FEARING, F.S. (1924). The factors influencing static equilibrium. *Journal of Comparative Psychology*, 4, 91-121.

FERGUSON, G.A. (1954). On learning and human ability. *Canadian Journal of Psychology*, 8, 95-112.

FISHER, M.B., BIRREN, J.E. & LEGGET, A.L. (1945). Standardization of two tests of equilibrium; the railwalking test and the ataxiagraph. *Journal of Experimental Psychology*, 35, 321-329.

FITTS, P.M. (1951). Engineering psychology and equipment design. In S.S. Stevens (Ed.), *Handbook of Experimental Psychology*. New York: Wiley.

FITTS, P.M. (1954). The information capacity of the human motor system in controlling the amplitude of movement. *Journal of Experimental Psychology*, 47, 381-391.

FITTS, P.M. (1964). Perceptual motor skill learning. In A.W. Melton (Ed.). *Categories of Human Learning*. New York: Academic Press.

FITTS, P.M. & PETERSON, J.R. (1964). Information capacity of discrete motor responses. *Journal of Experimental Psychology*, 67, 103-112.

FITTS, P.M. & POSNER, M.I. (1967). *Human Performance*. Belmont, Calif.: Brooks/Cole Publishing Co.

FLEISHMAN, E.A. (1964). *The structure and measurement of physical fitness*. Englewood Cliffs, New Jersey: Prentice Hall.

FLEISHMAN, E.A. (1965). The prediction of total task performance from prior practice on task components. *Human Factors*, 7, 18-27.

FLEISHMAN, E.A. (1966). Human abilities and the acquisition of skill. In E.A. Bilodeau (Ed.). *Aquisition of Skill*. New York: Academic Press.

FLEISHMAN, E.A. & HEMPEL, W.E. (1954). Changes in factor structure of a complex psychomotor test as a function of practice. *Psychometrika,* 19, 239-252.

FLEISHMAN, E.A. & HEMPEL, W.E. (1956). Factorial analysis of complex psychomotor performance and related skills. *Journal of Applied Psychology*, 40, 96-104.

FLEISHMAN, E.A. & ORNSTEIN, G.N. (1960). An analysis of pilot flying performance in terms of component abilities. *Journal of Applied Psychology*, 44, 146-155.

FLEISHMAN, E.A. & RICH, S. (1963). Role of kinesthetic and spatial visual abilities in perceptual motor learning. *Journal of Experimental Psychology*, 66, 6-11.

FRENCH, J.D. (1960). The reticular formation. In J. Field, J.W. Magoun and V.E. Hall (Eds.). *Handbook of Physiology, Vol. 2*. Baltimore: Williams and Wilkins.

FULTON, J.F. & PI-SUNER, J. (1928). A note concerning the probable function of various afferent end-organs in skeletal muscle. *American Journal of Physiology*, 83, 554-562.

GAGNE, R.M. & FLEISHMAN, E.A. (1959). *Psychology and Human Performance.* New York: Holt and Co.

GARDNER, E. (1950). Physiology of moveable joints. *Physiology Review,* **30,** 127-176.

GARDNER, E. & HADDAD, B. (1953). Pathways to the cerebral cortex for afferent fibres from the hindleg of the cat. *American Journal of Physiology,* **172,** 475-482.

GARNER, W.R. & HAKE, H.W. (1951). The amount of information in absolute judgement. *Psychological Review,* **58,** 446-459.

GARTEN, S. (1920). Uber die Grundlagung unserer Orien ierung irn Raum. (Cited in Howard and Templeton, 1966).

GELLHORN, E. (1948). The influence of alterations in posture of the limbs on cortically induced movements. *Brain,* **71** 26-33.

GERNANDT, B. (1949). Response of mammalian vestibular neurones to horizontal rotation and caloric stimulation. *Journal of Neurophysiology,* **12,** 173-184.

GERNANDT, B.E. (1964). Vestibular connections in the brainstem. In M.B. Bender (Ed.), *The Oculomotor System.* New York: Harper and Row.

GIBBS, C.B. (1954), The continuous regulation of skilled response by kinesthetic feedback. *British Journal of Psychology,* **45,** 24-39.

GIBBS, C.B. (1965). Probability learning in step-input tracking. *British Journal of Psychology,* **56,** 233-242.

GIBBS, C.B. (1970). Servo control systems in organisms and the transfer of skill. In D. Legge (Ed.), *Skills.* Harmondsworth: Penguin Books.

GIBBS, C.B. & LOGAN, O. (1965). Tests of the functions of proprioception and interaction of senses. *Perceptual and Motor Skills,* **20,** 433-442.

GIBSON, J.J. (1933). Adaptation, after effect and contrast in the perception of curved lines. *Journal of Experimental Psychology,* **16,** 1-31.

GIBSON, J.J. (1937). Adaptation with negative after effect. *Psychological Review,* **44,** 222-244.

GIBSON, J.J. (1966). *The Senses Considered as Perceptual Systems.* Boston: Houghton Mifflin Co.

GOETZINGER, C.P. (1961). A reevaluation of the Heath Railwalking Test. *Journal of Educational Research,* **54,** 187-191.

GOLDSCHEIDER, A. 1889. Untersuchungen über den Muskelsinn, cited in Boring, E.G. (1942).

GOLDSTONE, S., BOARDMAN, W.K. & LHAMON, W.T. (1958). Kinesthetic cues in the development of time concepts. *Journal of Genetic Psychology* **93,** 185-190.

GRANIT, R. (1955). *Receptors and Sensory Perception.* New Haven: Yale University Press.

GRANIT, R. & KAADA, B.R. (1952). Influence of stimulation of central nervous structures on muscle spindles in cat. *Acta Physiol. Scand.,* **27,** 130-150.

GRAYBIEL, A. & FREGLY, A.R. (1965). A new quantitative ataxia test battery. *N.A.S.A. Joint Report.*

GRAYBIEL, A., KERR, W.A. & BARTLEY, S.H. (1948). Stimulus thresholds of the semicircular canals as a function of angular acceleration. *American Journal of Psychology,* **61,** 21-36.

GREEN, D.M. (1960). Psychoacoustics and detection theory. *Journal of the Acoustical Society of America,* **32,** 1189-1203.

GROEN, J.J. (1961). The problems of the spinning top applied to the semicircular canals. *Confin. Neurol., Basel,* **21,** 454-455.

GROSE, J.E. (1967). Timing control in finger, arm, and whole body movements. *Research Quarterly,* **38,** 10-21.

GROSS E.A. & THOMPSON, H.L. (1957). Relationship of dynamic balance to speed and to ability in swimming. *Research Quarterly,* **28,** 342-346.

GROSSMAN, S.P. (1967). *A textbook of physiological psychology.* New York: Wiley & Sons, Inc.

GUTHRIE, E.R. (1952). *The Psychology of Learning,* (Rev. Ed.). New York: Harper and Row.

GUTHRIE, E.R. (1959). Association by contiguity. In S. Koch (Ed.), *Psychology: A Study of Science,* Vol. 2. New York: McGraw-Hill.

HALL, J.F. (1966). *The Psychology of Learning.* Philadelphia: J.B. Lippincott Company.

HAMILTON, C.R. (1964). Intermanual transfer of adaptation to prisms. *American Journal of Psychology,* **77,** 457-462.

HAY, J.C. & PICK, H.L. (1966). Visual and proprioceptive adaptation to optical displacement of the visual stimulus. *Journal of Experimental Psychology,* **71,** 150-158.

HAY, J.C., PICK, H.L. & IKEDA, K. (1965). Visual capture produced by prism spectacles. *Psychonomic Science,* **2,** 215-216.

HEBB, D.O. (1966). *A Textbook of Psychology.* Philadelphia: W.B. Saunders Co.

HELD, R. (1965). Plasticity in sensory-motor systems. *Scientific American,* 214. Reprinted in R.C. Atkinson (Ed.). *Contemporary Psychology.* San Francisco: W.H. Freeman and Company. 1971.

HELD, R. & FREEDMAN, S.J. (1963). Plasticity in human sensorimotor control. *Science,* 142, 455-462.

HELLEBRANDT, F.A., BRAUN, G. & TEPPER, R.H. (1937). The relation of the centre of gravity to the base of support in stance. *American Journal of Physiology,* **19,** 313-332.

HENRY, F. (1953). Dynamic kinesthetic perception and adjustment. *Research Quarterly,* **24,** 176-187.

HERBERT, M. (1963). Analysis of complex skill: vehicle driving. *Human Factors,* **5,** 363-372.

HICK, W.E. (1949). Reaction time for the amendment of a response. *Quarterly Journal of Experimental Psychology,* **1,** 175-179.

HILGARD, E.R. (1951). Methods and procedures in the study of learning. In S.S. Stevens (Ed.), *Handbook of Experimental Psychology*. New York: Wiley.

HILGARD, E.R. & BOWER, G.H. (1966). *Theories of Learning, (3rd. Edit)*. New York: Appleton-Century-Crofts.

HINTZMAN, D.L. (1965). Classification and aural coding in short-term memory. *Psychonomic Science*, 3, 161-162.

HINTZMAN, D.L. (1967). Articulatory coding in short-term memory. *Journal of Verbal Learning and Verbal Behaviour*, 6, 312-316.

HOFF, P.A. (1971). Scales of selected aspects of kinesthesis. *Perception and Psychophysics*, 9, 118-120.

HOLDING, D.H., (1965). *Principles of Training*. Oxford: Pergamon Press.

HOLDING, D.H. & MACRAE, A.W. (1964). Guidance, restriction and knowledge of results. *Ergonomics*, 7, 289-295.

HOLDING D.H. & MACRAE, A.W. (1966). Rate and force of guidance in perceptual motor tasks with reversed or random spatial correspondence. *Ergonomics*, 9, 289-296.

HONZIK, C.H. (1936). The sensory basis of maze learning in rats. *Comparative Psychological Monographs*, 13, No. 64.

HOWARD, I.P. (1966). Motor system. In J.A. Deutsch and D. Deutsch (Eds.), *Physiological Psychology*. Homewood, Ill.: The Dorsey Press.

HOWARD, I.P. & TEMPLETON, W.B. (1966). *Human Spatial Orientation*. New York: Wiley.

HOWLAND, D. & NOBLE, M.E. (1953). The effect of physical constants of a control on tracking performance. *Journal of Experimental Psychology*, 46, 353-360.

HULL, C.L. (1951). *Essentials of behaviour*. New Haven: Yale University Press.

HULL, C.L. (1952). *A behaviour system*. New York: John Wiley and Sons, Inc.

HUNT, C.C. & PAINTAL, A.S. (1958). Spinal regulation of fusimotor neurones. *Journal of Physiology*, 143, 195-212.

HUTTON, R.S. (1966). Kinesthetic after effect produced by walking on a gradient. *Research Quarterly*, 37, 368-374.

JAMES, W. (1890). *The Principles of Psychology*. New York: Holt, Rinehart and Winston.

JENKINS, J.E. & DALLENBACH, K.M. (1924). Obliviscence during sleep and waking. *American Journal of Psychology*, 35, 605-612.

JONES, M.B. (1966). Individual differences. In E.A. Bilodeau (Ed.). *Acquisition of Skill*. New York: Academic Press.

JONGKEES, L.B.W. & GROEN, J.J. (1946). The nature of the vestibular stimulus. *J. Laryng*, 61, 529-541.

JUNG, J. (1968). *Verbal Learning*. New York: Holt, Rinehart and Winston, Inc.

KAY, H. (1951). Learning of a serial task by different age groups. *Quarterly Journal of Experimental Psychology*, 3, 166-183.

KEELE, S.W. (1968). Movement control in skilled motor performance. *Psychological Bulletin*, 70, 387-403.

KERR, W.H. & WEINLUND, J.D. (1933). Muscular perceptivity as a trade test. *Journal of Applied Psychology*, 17, 550-558.

KIMBLE, G.A. (1961). *Hilgard and Marquis' Conditioning and Learning* (Second Edition). New York: Appleton-Century-Crofts.

KLEINKNECHT, F. & LUEG, W. (1924). Weitere Untersuchungen über Lagenbedächtnis und Empfindung am Neigunstuhl. (Cited in Howard and Templeton. 1966).

KLING, J.W. & RIGGS, L.A. (Eds.), (1971). *Woodworth and Schlosberg's Experimental Psychology*. New York: Holt, Rinehart and Winston, Inc.

KNAPP, B.N. (1963). *Skill in Sport*. London: Routledge and Kegan Paul.

KNAPP, H.D., TAUB, E. & BERMAN, A.J. (1963). Movements in monkeys with deafferented forelimbs. *Experimental Neurology*, 7, 305-315.

LANG, A. (1965). Perceptual behaviour of 8- to 10-week old human infants. *Psychonomic Science*, 4, 203-204.

LASHLEY, K.S. (1917). The accuracy of movement in the absence of excitation from the moving organ. *American Journal of Physiology*, 43, 169-194.

LASHLEY, K.S. & McCARTHY, D.A. (1926). The survival of the maze habit after cerebeller injuries. *Journal of Comparative Psychology*, 6, 423-434.

LASZLO, J.I. (1966). The performance of a simple motor task with kinesthetic sense loss. *Quarterly Journal of Experimental Psychology*, 18, 1-8.

LASZLO, J.I. (1967). Training of fast tapping with reduction of kinaesthetic, tactile, visual and auditory sensations. *Quarterly Journal of Experimental Psychology*, 19, 344-349.

LASZLO, J.I. & BAIRSTOW, P.J. (1971). Accuracy of movement, peripheral feedback and efference copy. *Journal of Motor Behaviour*, 3, 241-252.

LEE, J. & RING, P.A. (1954). The effect of local anaesthesia on the appreciation of passive movement of the great toe in man. *Journal of Physiology*, 123, 56-57.

LEGGE, D. (1965). Analysis of visual and proprioceptive components of motor skill by means of a drug. *British Journal of Psychology*, 56, 245-254.

LEONARD, J.A. (1966). Static and mobile balancing in blind children. *Bulletin of the British Psychological Society;* 19, 63, A24 (Abstract).

LINCOLN, R.S. (1956). Learning and retaining a rate of movement with the aid of kinesthetic and verbal cues. *Journal of Experimental Psychology*, 51, 199-204.

LLOYD, D.P.C. (1943). Neuron patterns controlling transmission of ipsilateral hindlimb reflexes in cat. *Journal of Neuro-physiology,* **6,** 298-315.

LLOYD, A.J. & CALDWELL, L.S. (1965). Accuracy of active and passive positioning of the leg on the basis of kinesthetic cues. *Journal of Comparative and Physiological Psychology,* **60,** 102-106.

LOCKE, L.F. (1969). Movement education—a description and critique. In R.C. Brown and B.J. Cratty, (Eds.), *New Perspectives of Man in Action.* Englewood Cliffs: Prentice Hall, Inc.

LORGE, I. & THORNDIKE, E.L. (1935). The influence of delay in the after effects of a connection. *Journal of Experimental Psychology,* **18,** 186-194.

LYNN, R. (1966). *Attention, Arousal and the Orientation Reaction.* Oxford: Pergamon Press.

MACCORQUODALE, K. (1948). Effects of angular acceleration and centrifugal force on non-visual space orientation during flight. *Journal of Aviation Medicine,* **19,** 146-157.

MACH, E. (1875). Grundinien der Lehre von den Bewegungsempfindungen, Leipzig: Englelmann.

MACKWORTH, J.F. (1970). *Vigilance and Attention.* Harmondsworth: Penguin Books.

MACRAE, A.W. & HOLDING, D.H. (1965). Guided practice in direct and reversed serial tracking. *Ergonomics,* **8,** 487-492.

MANN, C.W., BERTHELOT-BERRY, N.H. & DAUTERIVE, H.J. (1949). The perception of the vertical 1. visual and non-labyrinthine cues. *Journal of Experimental Psychology,* **39,** 538.

MARTENUIK, R.G. (1971). An informational analysis of active kinesthesis as measured by amplitude of movement. *Journal of Motor Behaviour,* **3,** 69-77.

MARTENUIK, R.G. & RYAN, M.L. (1972). Psychophysics of kinesthesis: angular movement. *Journal of Motor Behaviour,* **4,** 135-142.

MARTENUIK, R.G., SHIELDS, K.W. & CAMPBELL, S. (1972). Amplitude, position, timing and velocity as cues in reproduction of movement. *Perceptual and Motor Skills* **35,** 51-58.

MARX, M.H. (1970). *Learning: Interactions.* London: Collier-MacMillan Ltd.

MARX, M.H. (1970). *Learning: Theories.* London: Collier-MacMillan Ltd.

MATTHEWS, B.H.C. (1931). The response of a muscle spindle during active contraction of a muscle. *Journal of Physiology,* **72,** 153-174.

MATTHEWS, B.H.C. (1933). Nerve ending in mammalian muscle. *Journal of Physiology,* **78,** 1-53.

MATTHEWS, P.B.C. (1964). Muscle spindles and their motor control. *Physiological Review,* **44,** 219-288.

MCALLISTER, D.E. (1952). Retroactive facilitation and interference as a function of level of learning. *American Journal of Psychology,* **65,** 218-232.

MCCONCHIE, R.D. & RUTSCHMANN, J. (1970). Reliability of time estimation, effect of a preceding reproduction series on the reliability of subsequent verbal estimates of the same standard stimuli. *Perceptual and Motor Skills*, **31**, 51-55.

MCFARLAND, R.A. (1946). *Human Factors in Air Transport Design*. New York: McGraw-Hill.

MCGEOCH, J.A. (1932). Forgetting and the law of disuse. *Psychological Review*, **39**, 352-370.

MEREDITH, G.P. (1965). Editor's foreword in D.H. Holding's *Principles of Training*. Oxford: Pergamon Press.

MERTON, P.A. (1964). Human position sense and sense of effort. In symposia of the society for experimental biology, No. 18, *Homeostasis and Feedback Mechanisms*. Cambridge; Mass.: University Press.

MILES, W.R. (1950). Static equilibrium. In R.W. Gerard (Ed.), *Methods in Medical Research*, Vol. 3. Chicago: Year Book Publishers.

MILLER, G.A. (1956). The magical number seven, plus or minus two. Some limits on our capacity for processing information. *Psychological Review*, **63**, 81-97.

MILLER, G.A., GALANTER, E.H. & PRIBRAM, K.H. (1960). *Plans and the Structure of Behaviour*. New York: Holt, Rinehart and Winston, Inc.

MORGAN, C.T. & KING, R.A. (1956). *Introduction to Psychology*. New York: McGraw-Hill Book Co.

MORISON, R. (1969). *A Movement Approach to Educational Gymnastics*. London: Dent.

MORUZZI, G. (1950). *Problems in Cerebellar Physiology*. Springfield; Ill.: Thomas.

MOUNTCASTLE, V.B. (1957). Modality and topographic properties of single neurons of cat's somatic sensory cortex. *Journal of Neurophysiology*, **20**, 408-434.

MOUNTCASTLE, V.B., POGGIO, G.F. & WERNER, G. (1963). The relation of thalamic cell response to peripheral stimuli varied over an intensive continuum. *Journal of Neurophysiology*, **26**, 804-834.

MOWRER, O.H. (1947). On the dual nature of learning. A reinterpretation of 'conditioning' and 'problem solving'. *Harvard Educational Review*, **17**, 102-148.

MOWRER, O.H. (1960). *Learning Theory and Behavior*. New York: Wiley.

MUMBY, H.H. (1953). Kinesthetic acuity and balance related to wrestling ability. *Research Quarterly*, **24**, 327-330.

MUNN, N.L. (1955). *The Evolution and Growth of Human Behavior*. Boston: Houghton-Mifflin Co.

MUNSON, W.A. & KARLIN, J.E. (1956). The measurement of the human channel transmission characteristics. *Journal of the Acoustical Society of America*, **26**, 542-553.

MÜNSTERBERG, H. (1889). Beiträge zur experimentellen Psychologie. (Cited in W. James, 1890).

MURDOCK, B.B. (1971). *Human Memory*. New York: General Learning Press.

NAYLOR, J.C. & BRIGGS, G.E. (1963). Effects of task complexity and task organization on the relative efficiency of part and whole methods. *Journal of Experimental Psychology, 65*, 217-224.

NORTH, J.D. & LOMNICKI, Z.A. (1961). Further experiments on human operators in compensatory tracking tasks. *Ergonomics, 4*, 339-353.

NOTTERMAN, J.M. & PAGE, D.E. (1962). Evaluation of mathematically equivalent tracking systems. *Perceptual and Motor Skills, 15*, 683-716.

OSCARSSON, O. 1966. The projection of Group I muscle afferents to the cat cerebral cortex. In R. Granit (Ed.), *Muscular Afferents in Motor Control*. New York: Wiley & Sons.

PAILLARD, J. (1960). The patterning of skilled movements. In J. Field, H.W. Magoun and V.E. Hall, (Eds.). *Handbook of Physiology, Section 1, Vol. 3*. Washington: American Physiological Society.

PETERSON, L.R. & PETERSON, M.J. (1959). Short term retention of individual verbal items. *Journal of Experimental Psychology, 58*, 193-198.

PHILLIPS, B.E. (1941). The relation between certain phases of kinesthesis and performance during the early stages of acquiring two perceptuo-motor skills. *Research Quarterly, 12*, 571-586.

PHILLIPS, M. & SUMMERS, D. (1954). Relation of kinesthetic perception to motor learning. *Research Quarterly, 25*, 456-469.

POSNER, M.I. (1966). Components of skilled performance. *Science, 152*, 1712-1718.

POSNER, M.I. (1967). Characteristics of visual and kinesthetic memory codes. *Journal of Experimental Psychology, 75*, 103-107.

POSNER, M.I. & KONICK A.F. (1966). Short-term retention of visual and kinesthetic information. *Journal of Organisational Behaviour and Human Performance, 1*, 71-88.

POSTMAN, L. & GOGGIN, J. (1966). Whole versus part learning of paired associate lists. *Journal of Experimental Psychology, 71*, 867-877.

POULTON, E.C. (1966). Tracking Behaviour, in E.A. Bilodeau (Ed.), *Acquisition of Skill*. New York: Academic Press.

POULTON, E.C. (1957). On prediction in skilled movements. *Psychological Bulletin, 54*, 467-478.

PROVINS, K.A. (1958). The effect of peripheral nerve block on the appreciation and execution of finger movements. *Journal of Physiology, 143*, 55-67.

QUESADA, D.C. & SCHMIDT, R.A. (1970). A test of the Adams-Creamer decay hypothesis for motor response timing. *Journal of Motor Behaviour, 2*, 273-283.

RAGSDALE, C.E. (1950). Learning and instruction, Part I. *49th Yearbook of the National Society for the Study of Education.* Chicago: University of Chicago Press.

RANDALL, M. (1961). *Basic Movement.* London: Bell and Sons.

RAUBER, A. (1865). Vater'sche Körper der Bander-und periostnerven und ihre Beziehung zum sogenannten Muskelsinne (Cited in Boring 1942).

ROBINSON, P.D. (1969). *Development of tests to measure fine and gross proprioception in children.* Unpublished doctoral dissertation, Michigan State University.

ROCK, I. & HARRIS, C.S. (1967). Vision and touch. *Scientific American,* 216, 96-107.

ROCK, I. & VICTOR, J. (1964). Vision and touch: an experimentally created conflict between the two senses. *Science,* 143, 594-596.

ROLOFF, L. (1953). Kinesthesis in relation to the learning of selected motor skills. *Research Quarterly,* 24, 210-217.

RONCO, P.G. (1963). An experimental quantification of kinesthetic sensation: Extent of arm movement. *Journal of Psychology,* 55, 227-238.

ROSS, H.E. & GREGORY, R.L. (1964). Is the Weber fraction a function of physical or perceived input? *Quarterly Journal of Experimental Psychology,* 16, 116-122.

RUCH, T.C. (1951). Motor Systems. In S.S. Stevens (Ed.), *Handbook of Experimental Psychology.* New York: Wiley & Sons.

RUCH, T.C. & PATTON, H.D. (1965). *Physiology and Biophysics.* Philadelphia: W.B. Saunders Co.

RUFFINI, A. (1898). On the minute anatomy of the neuromuscular spindles of the cat, and on their physiological significance. *Journal of Physiology,* 23, 190-208.

SCHMIDT, R.A. (1971). Retroactive interference and amount of original learning in verbal and motor tasks. *Research Quarterly,* 42, 314-326.

SCHMIDT, R.A. (1971). Proprioception and the timing of motor responses. *Psychological Bulletin,* 76, 383-393.

SCHMIDT, R.A. & CHRISTINA, R.W. (1969). Proprioception as a mediator in the timing of motor responses. *Journal of Experimental Psychology,* 81, 303-307.

SCOTT, M.G. (1955). Measurement of kinesthesis. *Research Quarterly,* 26, 324-341.

SEASHORE, H.G. (1938). Measurement of dynamic balance with a walking beam test. *Psychological Bulletin,* 35, 714, (Abstract).

SEASHORE, R.H. & BAVELAS, A. (1941). The function of knowledge of results in Thorndike's linedrawing experiment, *Psychological Review,* 48, 155-164.

SEKULER, R.W. (1965). Discrimination of hefted weights. *Psychonomic Science,* 3, 255-256.

SHERRINGTON, C.S. (1894). On the anatomical constitution of nerves of skeletal muscles; with remarks on recurrent fibres in the ventral spinal nerve root. *Journal of Physiology.* **17**, 211-258.

SHERRINGTON, C.S. (1906). *The Integrative Action of the Nervous System.* New Haven: Yale University Press.

SLATER-HAMMEL, A.T. (1956). Performance of selected groups of male college students on the Reynolds balance tests. *Research Quarterly,* **27**, 348-351.

SLINGER, R.T. & HORSLEY, V. (1906). Upon the orientation of points in space by muscular, arthroidal and tactile senses of the upper limbs in normal individuals and in blind persons. *Brain,* **29**, 1-27.

SMITH, J.L. (1969). Kinesthesis: a model for movement feedback. In R.C. Brown and B.J. Cratty (Eds.), *New Perspectives of Man in Action.* Englewood Cliffs: Prentice-Hall Inc.

SMITH, K.U. (1962). *Delayed Sensory Feedback and Behavior.* Philadelphia: Saunders.

SMITH, K.U. (1966). Cybernetic Theory and analysis of learning. In E.A. Bilodeau, (Ed.), *Acquisition of Skill.* New York: Academic Press.

SMITH, K.U. & SMITH, M.F. (1966). *Cybernetic Principles of Learning and Educational Design.* New York: Holt.

SOKOLOV, E.N. (1960). Neuronal models and the orienting reflex. In M.A. Brazier (Ed.), *The Central Nervous System and Behaviour.* New York: J. Macy.

SOLLEY, C.M. (1956). Reduction of error with practice in perception of the postural vertical. *Journal of Experimental Psychology,* **52**, 329-337.

SOLLEY, C.M. (1960). Influence of head tilt, body tilt and practice reduction of error in perception of the postural vertical. *Journal of Genetic Psychology,* **62**, 69-74.

SOLOMON, R.L. & TURNER, L.H. (1962). Discriminative classical conditioning in dogs paralyzed by curare can later control discriminative avoidance responses in the normal state. *Psychological Review,* **69**, 202-219.

SPEARS, W.C. (1964). Assessment of visual preference and discrimination in the four-month old infant. *Journal of Comparative and Physiological Psychology,* **57**, 381-386.

SPENCE, K.W. (1947). The role of secondary reinforcement in delayed reward learning. *Psychological Review,* **54**, 1-8.

SPERLING, G. (1960). The information available in brief visual presentations. *Psychological Monographs,* **74**, 11.

SPERLING, G. (1967). Successive approximations to a model for short term memory. *Acta Psychologica,* **27**, 285-292.

SPRAGUE, J.M. & CHAMBERS, W.W. (1954). Control of posture by reticular formation and cerebellum in the intact, anesthetized and unanesthetized and in the decerebrate cat. *American Journal of Physiology*, 176, 52-64.

STAATS, A.W. & STAATS, C.K. (1963). *Complex Human Behaviour*. New York: Holt, Rinehart & Winston.

STEVENS, J.C. & MACK, J.D. (1959). Scales of apparent force. *Journal of Experimental Psychology*, 58 405-413.

STEVENS, S.S. (1951). (Ed.) *Handbook of Experimental Psychology*. New York: Wiley.

STEVENS, S.S. (1961). To honor Fechner and repeal his law. *Science*, 133, 80-86.

STEVENS, S.S. (1962). The surprising simplicity of sensory metrics. *American Psychologist*, 17, 29-39.

STEVENS, S.S. & GALANTER, E.H. (1957). Ratio scales and category scales for a dozen continua. *Journal of Experimental Psychology*, 54, 377-411.

STEVENS, S.S. & STONE, G. (1959). Finger span: Ratio scale, category scale and JND scale. *Journal of Experimental Psychology*, 57, 91-95.

SWETS, J.A. (1961). Detection theory and psychophysics. *Psychometrika*. 26, 49-63.

TANNER, W.P. & SWETS, J.A. (1954). A decision-making theory of visual detection. *Psychological Review*, 61, 401-409.

TAUB, E., BACON, R.C. & BERMAN, A.J. (1965). Acquisition of a trace conditioned avoidance response after deafferentation of the responding limb. *Journal of Comparative and Physiological Psychology*, 59, 275-279.

TAUB, E. & BERMAN, A.J. (1963). Avoidance conditioning in the absence of relevant proprioceptive and exteroceptive feedback. *Journal of Comparative and Physiological Psychology*, 56, 1012-1016.

THORNDIKE, E.L. (1898). Animal intelligence: An experimental study of associative processes in animals. *Psychological Review*, Monograph Supplement, 2, 8.

THORNDIKE, E.L. (1911). *Animal Intelligence*. New York: MacMillan.

THORNDIKE, E.L. (1927). The law of effect. *American Journal of Psychology*, 39, 212-222.

THORPE, W.H. (1956). *Learning and Instinct in Animals*. London: Methuen.

THURSTONE, L.L. (1947). *Multiple Factor Analysis*. Chicago: University of Chicago Press.

TOLMAN, E.C. (1932). *Purposive Behavior in Animals and Men*. New York: Appleton-Century-Crofts.

TRAVIS, R.C. (1944). A new stabilometer for measuring dynamic equilibrium in the standing position. *Journal of Experimental Psychology*, 34, 418-424.

TRAVIS, R.C. (1945). Experimental analysis of dynamic and static equilibrium. *Journal of Experimental Psychology*, 35, 216-234.

TROWBRIDGE, M.A. & CASON, H. (1932). An experimental study of

Thorndike's theory of learning. *Journal of Genetic Psychology*, 7, 245-260.

VINCE, M.A. (1948). The intermittency of control movements and the psychological refractory period. *British Journal of Psychology*, 38, 149-157.

VINCE, M.A. (1948). Corrective movements in a pursuit task. *Quarterly Journal of Experimental Psychology*, 1, 85-103.

von HOLST, E. (1954). Relations between the central nervous system and the peripheral organs. *British Journal of Animal Behaviour*, 2, 89-94.

von WRIGHT, J.M. (1957). A note on the role of guidance in learning. *British Journal of Psychology*, 48, 133-137.

WALLACH, H., KRAVITZ, J.H. & LINDAUER, J. (1963). A passive condition for rapid adaptation to displaced visual direction. *American Journal of Psychology*, 76, 568-578.

WALLON, EVART-CHMIELNISKI & SAUTEREY. (1958). Equilbre statique, equilibre en mouvement; double lateralization (entre 5 ans et 15 ans). *Enfance*, 1, 1-29.

WAPNER, S., WERNER, H. & CHANDLER, K.A. (1951). Experiments on sensory-tonic field theory of perception: I. Effect of extraneous stimulation on the visual perception of verticality. *Journal of Experimental Psychology*, 42, 341-345.

WATSON, J.B. (1926). Recent experiments on how we lose and change our emotional equipment. In C. Murchison (Ed.), *Psychologies of 1925*. Worcester, Mass.: Clark University Press.

WEISS, B. (1954). The role of proprioceptive feedback in positioning responses. *Journal of Experimental Psychology*, 47, 215-224.

WELFORD, A.T. (1965). Performance, biological mechanisms and age: a theoretical sketch. In A.T. Welford and J.E. Birren (Eds.), *Behavior, Ageing and the Nervous System*. Springfield, Ill.: Charles C. Thomas.

WELFORD, A.T. (1968). *Fundamentals of Skill*. London: Methuen and Co. Ltd.

WENDT, G.R. (1951). Vestibular functions. In. S.S. Stevens (Ed.), *Handbook of Experimental Psychology*. New York: Wiley & Sons, Inc.

WERTHEIMER, M. & LEVENTHAL, C.M. (1958). Permanent satiation phenomena with kinesthetic figural after effects. *Journal of Experimental Psychology*, 55, 255-257.

WEST, L.J. (1967). Vision and kinesthesis in the acquisition of typewriting skill. *Journal of Applied Psychology*, 51, 161-166.

WHITING, H.T.A. (1969). *Acquiring Ball Skill*. London: Bell.

WIEBE, V.R. (1954). A study of tests of kinesthesis. *Research Quarterly*, 25, 222-230.

WIENER, N. (1948). *Cybernetics*. New York: Technological press of M.I.T. and John Wiley and Sons.

WIERSMA, C.A.G. (1963). Movement receptors in deapod crustaeca. *Journal of Marine Biological Association,* **38,** 157-169.

WING, M.E. (1963). The response of the otolith organs to tilt. *Acta oto-laryng.,* **56,** 537-545.

WITKIN, H.A. & WAPNER, S. (1950). Visual factors in the maintenance of upright posture. *American Journal of Psychology,* **63,** 31-50.

WOODWORTH, R.S. (1899). Accuracy of voluntary movement. *Psychological Review, Monograph Supplement,* **3,** 13.

ZAHORIK, D.M. (1972). Subject strategies and interference in a discrete motor task. *Psychonomic Science,* **28,** 349-351.

ZAPOROZHETS, A.V. (1961). A.V. The origin and development of conscious control of movements in man. In N. O'Connor (Ed.), *Recent Soviet Psychology.* Oxford: Pergamon Press.

Authors Index

Subject Index